A GUIDE TO RESIDENTIAL
WOOD HEATING

Library and Archives Canada Cataloguing in Publication

Guide to Residential Wood Heating 66067

Pub. aussi en français sous le titre : Le guide du chauffage résidentiel 66068

Priced, separate English and French - print publication.
Sent request to Library Archives - George Duck. MB

ISBN 978-0-660-19848-4
Cat. no.: NH15-436/2008E
1. Stoves, Wood--Handbooks, manuals, etc. 2. Stoves, Wood--Safety measures.
3. Dwellings--Heating and ventilation--Canada. 4. Fuelwood.
5. Fireplaces. I. Canada Mortgage and Housing Corporation.

TH7437G84 2008   697'.04   C2008-980309-4

Printed in Canada
Produced by CMHC

This edition of *A Guide to Residential Wood Heating* is based on previous editions, which were written, produced and distributed by Natural Resources Canada and Canada Mortgage and Housing Corporation. The illustrations in this edition are from the 1993 edition.
CMHC thanks all authors and reviewers of this Guide.

A Guide to Residential Wood Heating

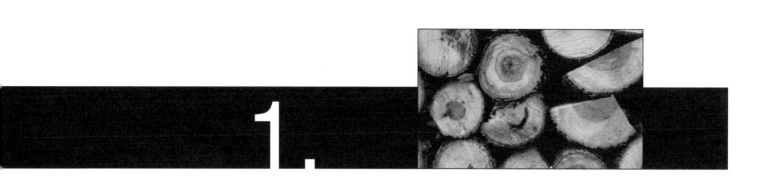

1. INTRODUCTION

If you heat with wood now or are considering the use of wood fuel for home heating, this book is for you.

If you heat with wood now or are considering the use of wood fuel for home heating, this book is for you. Wood as a home energy source differs in important ways from all the other options. Heating with wood can be challenging because of the physical demands involved. Special knowledge and skills are needed to successfully use this hands-on home heating option. In this book you will find much of the information needed to make sure your wood heat system is safe. You will also find helpful tips on how to operate and maintain it effectively.

Just as with all energy sources, heating with wood has both advantages and disadvantages. Some of the advantages are that wood is a renewable energy resource that does not need much processing. Many users like the fact that heating with wood makes their households self-sufficient for heating and secure during an electrical power failure since firewood burning appliances can operate without electricity. Burning wood from local sources means a double economic benefit in the form of savings to the household budget, and energy payments that circulate locally instead of going to distant energy companies. Some people enjoy cutting, splitting and stacking firewood and treat it as part of their physical fitness routine. Most people find the beauty of the natural wood fire hard to resist and many couldn't imagine living a winter in Canada without it.

There are disadvantages too. The most serious problem is air pollution caused by older stoves, fireplaces and furnaces that can't burn the wood completely, and by users who don't know how to burn wood properly. Even the most advanced wood heating technologies produce more air emissions in the form of small particles than the conventional heating fuels like oil and gas. Heating with wood means that household members must be involved in managing the fire, the fuel supply and doing regular maintenance jobs like ash removal. All these tasks take time and therefore have a cost. Wood fuel is bulky so a winter's supply takes up a lot of space. There are practical limits to the number of households in Canada that could be heated with wood because of the damage that could be caused to the forest resource and to the air quality in large cities.

Although wood was Canada's traditional fuel and was the main energy source until about 150 years ago, there have been major advances in wood burning over the past 25 years. These have made wood burning safer, more efficient and convenient than ever before. Some of these advances include:

- New firebox designs are capable of burning the wood more completely, cleanly and at higher efficiencies.
- A new type of door glass can withstand the heat, and a technology keeps the glass clear for days at a time, allowing efficient heating to be combined with viewing of the fire.

- Pellet stoves that use compressed wood and other biomass wastes are capable of providing at least 24 hours of unattended heating.

- Reliable installation safety standards provide clear guidelines for safe installation.

- Training and professional certification programs for installers and inspectors mean that you can get dependable advice and service.

As recently as 1980, most serious wood burning was done with basement wood furnaces or simple, black, wood stoves. Now, all that has changed. The majority of new wood heating installations are attractive, advanced-technology stoves and fireplaces located in main living areas. Properly installed and located wood heaters are able to provide most or all of the heat for a home, while at the same time offering the beauty of a visible fire.

Canadian houses have also become more energy efficient, with more insulation, more effective air barriers and sealed doors and windows. These changes have made houses easier to heat, but have also meant that wood-burning systems must be more carefully designed so they will function properly within the tightly sealed house environment. The keys to safe and successful wood burning are good planning, careful installation and proper operation. This book is intended to help you plan a successful installation and to use your wood-burning system in the most safe and effective way.

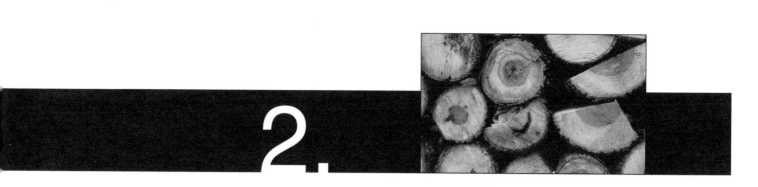

2.

WOOD BURNING AND THE ENVIRONMENT

Regardless of the fuel you choose to heat your home, its use will have impacts on the environment.

Regardless of the fuel you choose to heat your home, its use will have impacts on the environment. When it is not done properly, the burning of wood can have negative impacts on both indoor and outdoor air quality. Smouldering, smoky fires that produce a plume of blue-grey smoke from the chimney are the main cause of wood heat-related air pollution. Wood smoke can be harmful when it is breathed in by humans.

You can control the amount of pollution from your wood heating activities in a number of ways.

- Select an advanced technology stove, fireplace, furnace or boiler that is certified clean burning by the U.S. Environmental Protection Agency (EPA). These certified, clean-burning appliances reduce smoke emissions by as much as 90 per cent compared to conventional appliances.

- Select an appliance of the correct size and, if it is a stove or fireplace, locate it in the main living area to make the most effective use of the heat it produces.

- Use a suitable, correctly installed chimney, sized to match to your appliance.

- Avoid smouldering fires by learning to use the burn techniques covered later in this book. By using these techniques you can probably reduce the amount of smoke produced by as much as half.

- Burn only seasoned firewood that is split to the right size for your appliance. Never burn garbage, plastics, painted or treated wood, plywood, particle board, cardboard or salt water driftwood.

- Make your house more energy efficient so you will use less fuel to heat it. Less fuel consumption means less environmental impact.

Advanced Technology Appliances

You can identify advanced technology appliances because they are certified as clean burning by the U.S. Environmental Protection Agency (EPA). A label on the appliance will confirm that it is certified. The Canadian Standards Association has developed a similar standard, called CSA B415.1, but as of 2008 few appliances have been certified to this standard.

There are big differences in efficiency and performance between conventional stoves and the advanced, EPA-certified models. On average, advanced stoves are about one-third more efficient and produce about 90 per cent less smoke than conventional stoves.

When shopping for a new wood stove, fireplace, furnace or boiler, ask the retailer to show you the advanced technology models. You will find that the best-built units from the most reputable manufacturers are all EPA-certified advanced technology models.

Throughout this book, when advanced technology appliances are mentioned, you will know that EPA low-emission certification is what makes them advanced.

Low-Emission Wood Burning Technology

Over the past 25 years researchers and appliance designers have developed technologies that can reduce the amount of smoke and other pollutants produced by wood-burning appliances. These technologies are aimed at burning off the smoke before it leaves the firebox. This is not an easy task because to burn, the smoke must be extremely hot, have adequate oxygen available and have enough time to burn before being cooled.

Advanced technology wood-burning products have been highly successful, not just in reducing pollution and increasing the efficiency of wood heating, but also among Canadian householders who have accepted the technologies with enthusiasm. Already 40 per cent of wood stoves in use in Canada are advanced technology models.

There are three different combustion technologies that successfully reduce smoke pollution: catalytic, non-catalytic and densified pellet combustion technology.

Catalytic Combustion

A catalyst is a substance that affects a chemical reaction without being consumed in the process. The catalysts used in wood-burning appliances are coated ceramic honeycombs through which the exhaust gas is routed. The catalytic coating lowers the ignition temperature of the gases as they pass through. This allows catalytic appliances to operate at low firing rates while still burning cleanly.

Because the catalyst causes a restriction to gas flow through the appliance, these units always include a bypass damper into the flue. The damper is opened when the appliance is loaded and until a hot fire is established, then it is closed, forcing the gases through the combustor for an extended clean burn. The catalytic element degrades as it is used so it must be replaced after between two and six years of use. Catalytic combustion is used in fewer appliances now than in the past.

Non-Catalytic Combustion

Non-Catalytic combustion systems create the conditions necessary to burn the combustible gases without the use of catalysts. The technology has three main characteristics:

- firebox insulation to keep temperatures high;

- baffle plates to reflect heat back into the firebox, to create the gas turbulence needed for complete combustion and to give the gases a long and hot enough route so they will burn before being cooled; and,

- a heated secondary air supply that is usually fed to the fire above the fuel bed through ducts with small holes.

When a non-catalytic stove is burning, you will often see little jets of flame coming from these small air inlet holes. This is because the combustion air is hot enough when it enters the firebox to mix with the gases and produce flames. Non-catalytic combustion has become the dominant advanced technology used in firewood burning appliances.

Densified Pellet Technology

Pellets are dried ground wood or other biomass waste compressed into small cylinders about 6 mm (1/4 in.) in diameter and 25 mm (1 in.) long. The pressure and heat created during their production binds the pellets together without the need for additives. Pellet-burning appliances include a hopper to hold at least 20 kg (44lb.) of fuel and a screw auger to move the pellets from the hopper into the combustion chamber. Pellets usually burn cleanly because they are fed to the combustion chamber at a controlled rate and are matched with the right amount of combustion air. Pellet-burning appliances are generally able to operate at lower emission levels than natural firewood appliances.

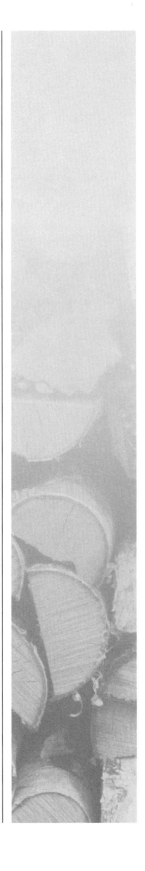

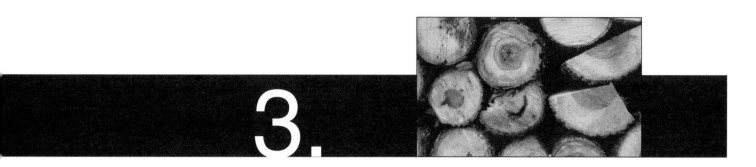

3.

WOOD HEATING OPTIONS

There are several different types of wood-heating appliances to choose from. Each type is intended for a particular use, and each has its own set of advantages and disadvantages.

There are several different types of wood-heating appliances to choose from. Each type is intended for a particular use, and each has its own set of advantages and disadvantages. Among the range of options, there are two general categories: space heaters and central systems.

Space Heaters

The space heater category is by far the largest and most popular, and includes wood stoves, cook stoves, pellet stoves, fireplaces, fireplace inserts and masonry heaters.

A space heater is defined as an appliance intended to heat a space directly, as distinct from a central heating furnace or boiler, which supplies its heat to the house through a system of ducts or water pipes. In the past, when houses were poorly insulated and drafty, a space heater could be expected only to heat the room it was installed in and perhaps an adjacent area. Modern houses conserve energy more effectively and need much less heat to stay warm. It is now possible for a single space heater to provide the total heat requirements for an average-size modern home.

This cast iron stove delivers radiant heat from its front, sides and top.

Like any effective heating system, a space heater installation takes careful planning to be successful. If you intend to provide a major part of your home heating needs with a space heater, you should consider two important matters. First, the heater should be located in the area where the family spends most of its time, and second, a means to distribute heat to other parts of the house may be necessary. These conditions are not usually difficult to meet, but they do need planning.

Wood Stoves

A wood stove is the most common, flexible and inexpensive space heating option. A wood stove can be located almost anywhere there is enough space and where its chimney can be properly routed. The ideal wood stove installation has the unit located centrally in the main floor living area of the house, with the flue pipe running straight up from the stove flue collar into the chimney. This installation design provides the best performance and needs the least maintenance.

Rules for Single-Wall Flue Pipe Assemblies

- Minimum clearance from combustible material: 450 mm (18 in.).

- The minimum clearance may be reduced by 50 per cent to 225 mm (9 in.) if suitable shielding is installed either on the pipe or on the combustible surface.

- Maximum overall length of straight pipe: 3 m (10 ft.).

- Maximum unsupported horizontal length: 1 m (3 ft.).

- Maximum number of 90-degree elbows: 2

- Minimum upward slope towards the chimney: 20 mm/m (1/4 in/ft.).

- The crimped ends (male) of the sections must be oriented towards the appliance.

- Each joint in the assembly must be fastened with at least three screws, including the connections at the appliance flue collar and chimney.

Heat Output: Wood stoves range in output from small ones designed to heat a single room, to large stoves able to heat whole houses. Large stoves can be used most effectively in houses of open plan design where the heat readily circulates to other areas. Selecting the right stove to match your needs can be tricky because its performance is not necessarily related to the way it looks. The best guide to heating capacity is firebox size rather than the overall size of the stove. A stove that is too small for the space it must heat will have to be loaded often and may deteriorate from being fired constantly at full output. A stove that is too large will overheat the space and be turned down too low much of the time, producing smoky, polluting fires. Note that, because of their higher efficiency, advanced stoves can usually have slightly smaller fireboxes than equivalent conventional stoves. The best way to choose a stove that is sized correctly for your needs is to get advice from an experienced wood stove retailer. Since experienced dealers know the performance of each of their stoves, they can help you match a stove to your heating goals.

Design: Some aspects of the design of wood stoves are related more to personal preference than to performance. For example, there are no clear performance differences between cast iron or plate steel construction or between painted or enamelled finishes. However, there is a difference between stoves that deliver their heat to the room mainly by direct radiation compared to those that deliver heat mainly by the convection flow of warm air. Radiant stoves send their heat out in all directions. The surface of objects, such as walls, floors, ceilings, furniture and people that face the appliance, are warmed.

Cast iron stoves and those with heavy steel plate surfaces are often of the radiant type. Convection stoves heat air that flows between the stove body and a sheet metal shield or casing.

When you shop for a new stove, you will notice that most modern stoves have a blend of both radiant and convection characteristics.

That is, the back and sides may have shields behind which air flows, whereas the front and top have radiant surfaces. In operation, these stoves produce both radiant and convective heat and can be suitable for most installations.

While the heating efficiency of radiant and convection stoves is about the same, there are advantages in using one or the other type depending on the details of the installation. For example, a stove with mainly radiant surfaces is effective in a relatively open area where the radiant warmth is dispersed. A radiant stove in a small room can make people feel uncomfortably warm. The heat from a radiant stove is somewhat more difficult to distribute to other areas of the home.

The shielded surfaces of a more convective stove don't get as hot as radiant surfaces and this can make a stove with shielded sides a better choice for a small room where furniture must be close to the installation.

Installation: A typical wood stove installation consists of the following components, starting from the floor level:

- a floor pad to protect flooring or carpets from embers which might fall from the stove during loading or ash removal;
- the stove itself;
- the flue pipe that connects the flue collar of the stove to the chimney; and expels the exhaust gases to the outdoors.

Each part of the space heater system deserves careful attention during installation to produce an effective heating system.

Wood-fired cook stoves are great for cooking food, but are not as effective as wood stoves for space heating.

Pellet appliances have some advantages over firewood burning appliances and also some disadvantages. In general, householders looking for convenience, automatic operation and neatness may find a pellet appliance desirable. Those who highly value low cost, self-sufficiency and heating security would find a regular wood stove more suitable.

Cook Stoves

Wood-fired stoves are designed for both surface cooking and oven baking, and may also have a low-temperature warming oven and a way to heat wash water. Cook stoves can also be used to heat limited areas, but space heating is not their main function. There are no advanced technology cook stoves, so their smoke emissions are higher and efficiency is lower than advanced wood stoves. Despite their limitations, cook stoves can be used successfully as space heaters for small, very well insulated houses.

Pellet Stoves

Although pellet-burning fireplace inserts, furnaces and boilers are available, by far the most common form of pellet appliance is space heating stoves. Pellet appliances are more complicated internally than wood stoves. They usually have three motorized systems. An auger moves the fuel from the storage hopper to the combustion chamber. An exhaust fan forces the exhaust gases into the venting system and draws in combustion air. Finally, a circulating fan forces air through the heat exchanger and into the room. Battery backup systems can be used to run pellet appliances during electrical power failures, but only for relatively short periods.

Pellet burners have several advantages over appliances that burn natural firewood:

- Their automatic operation is convenient. One hopper load of fuel can last 24 hours or more.

- Pellet stoves can produce a steady heat output and some are controlled with a wall thermostat.

- The fuel is supplied in bags, which store neatly.

- The fuel is always dry and ready to burn when purchased.

- Pellet appliances use a special vent that costs less to install than wood stove chimneys.

- Their smoke emissions are usually lower than those of advanced wood stoves.

Balancing these advantages are some limitations that you may wish to consider:

- Pellet appliances tend to cost more than firewood burners.
- Pellet fuel is more expensive than firewood in many areas.
- Pellet fuel cannot be made by householders so it must be purchased.
- Pellet stoves need electricity to operate auger motors and fans.
- The fire produced by a pellet stove does not have the natural appearance of a wood fire.

Conventional Fireplaces

Most fireplaces are built into the structure of the house and, in modern times, have been used mainly for fire viewing rather than heating. They are either site-built using masonry materials like brick or stone, or are factory-built from steel. Traditional fireplaces are ineffective for home heating and tests have shown that they can actually produce a negative energy efficiency by drawing a large amount of warm air out of the house while delivering little heat. This poor performance is because they are intended only for fire viewing and do not include the features needed to convert the fuel to useful heat, such as gasketed doors, carefully designed combustion chambers and heat exchangers. Conventional fireplaces also pollute the indoor and outdoor air more than advanced wood heating appliances.

If you already have a conventional masonry fireplace that you want to upgrade, you have some options, but only the third one in the list is truly effective:

- You could install a glass door assembly. The door will not improve energy efficiency, but might reduce the leakage of air when the fireplace is not in use.
- You could install a tubular grate or special firebox liner in an attempt to improve the fireplace's heating efficiency. These options are not usually effective because the improvement would be minor, and are not recommended because continuous use could cause dangerous overheating.
- You could install an advanced technology fireplace insert or hearthmount stove. These units are effective heaters that many Canadians use to reduce home heating costs. Modern inserts provide an excellent view of the fire, so the fireplace can still serve its original purpose.

Advanced Fireplaces

If you are planning to install a new fireplace, you can combine the beauty of a fireplace with the heating power of a wood stove by choosing an advanced technology fireplace. The same technologies used in wood stoves to meet regulated smoke emission limits

Advanced technology fireplaces combine the decorative flexibility of traditional fireplaces with the clean burning and high efficiency of advanced wood stoves.

An insert can be installed in an existing masonry fireplace to improve its efficiency and reduce the chances of cold air, odors and smoke spilling into the room.

are also used in these specialized factory-built fireplaces. The best examples of these fireplaces can be as effective for home heating as a good wood stove and are certified for low emissions.

The firebox and heat exchanger of these fireplaces is surrounded by an insulated sheet metal casing, allowing installation against combustible construction. A wood or steel stud frame sheathed with drywall or other materials is built to enclose the sides and rear. The front of the fireplace can be trimmed with ceramic tiles, brick or stone slices and a decorative mantel can be added. In most cases these fireplaces can be installed on a normal house floor without the need of a foundation or reinforcement.

Room air is drawn in through a grill under the firebox, passed through a heat exchanger and returned to the room either through a wide grill at the top of the fireplace body or through ducts which can be routed to grills above the fireplace or into other rooms beside, behind or even below the fireplace. These fireplaces offer features that can meet both esthetic and heating objectives, but their installation is complicated and should be left to trained professionals.

Fireplace Inserts

A fireplace insert is a specially designed wood stove intended for installation within the firebox of a masonry fireplace. Inserts are used to convert conventional masonry fireplaces into effective heating systems. An insert firebox is surrounded by an outer shell. Room air flows between the insert body and the outer shell where it is heated before being returned to the room. Most of the heat is delivered to the room instead of being trapped behind the insert in the masonry structure. A decorative face plate covers the space between the insert and the fireplace opening.

Installation codes require that a stainless steel chimney liner be installed from the insert flue collar to the top of the chimney. Correctly installed, an advanced fireplace insert can be almost as efficient as a free-standing wood stove. There are a few special inserts that can be installed in factory-built fireplaces. If you want to improve the performance of your conventional factory-built fireplace, ask a wood heating dealer if any inserts are certified for use with your fireplace.

A hearthmount stove is an option for upgrading the performance of a masonry fireplace. Hearthmounts are wood stoves mounted in front of or inside the fireplace and vented through the fireplace throat. They must also be vented through a stainless steel liner that is continuous to the top of the chimney. Only certain wood stoves can be used as hearthmounts. The certification label and installation instructions indicate if the unit can be vented through a fireplace.

Masonry Heaters

Masonry heaters have a long history in Northern Europe and have been shown to be efficient and effective for home heating. They operate on a different principle than the other advanced technology appliances. Masonry heaters use tonnes of mass in the form of bricks or stone to store and later release the heat they produce. The core of the heater is built from high-temperature firebrick and pre-cast components that form the firebox and heat transfer passages. To complete the heater, the core is then surrounded by brick or stone. With a masonry heater, one or two fires per day are built to provide the heat needed for the home. The wood is burned quickly and the fire is allowed to go out while the heat stored in the masonry continues to radiate warmth for many hours. Masonry heaters are more costly than other wood heating systems and are best suited to heating energy-efficient houses of moderate size. The Masonry Heater Association has developed a professional certification program for heater masons. The use of a certified mason is the best way to ensure a successful heater installation.

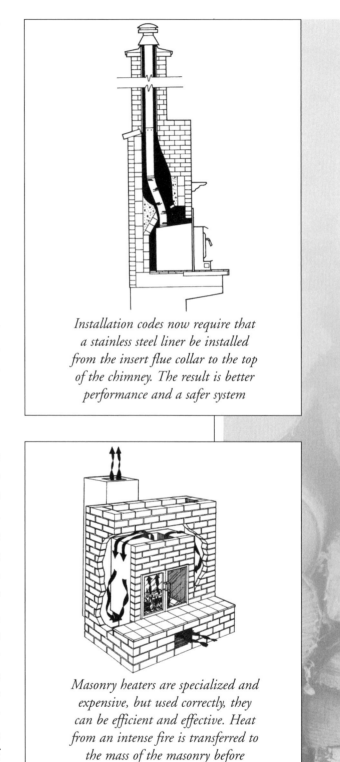

Installation codes now require that a stainless steel liner be installed from the insert flue collar to the top of the chimney. The result is better performance and a safer system

Masonry heaters are specialized and expensive, but used correctly, they can be efficient and effective. Heat from an intense fire is transferred to the mass of the masonry before being radiated to the room.

CENTRAL HEATING SYSTEMS
Furnaces and Boilers

A central heating system uses a network of air ducts or water pipes to distribute heat to all rooms of the house. Furnaces heat air, which is forced through ducts with a fan. Boilers heat water that is pumped through pipes to heat floors or radiators.

Central heating with wood-fired furnaces and boilers is not as common as it once was. Part of the reason is that our houses are more energy efficient and easier to heat with stoves and fireplaces that also provide a view of the fire. Another reason is that advanced technologies were not used in furnaces and boilers until recently so their efficiency was low. Even today, only a few central wood burning systems have proven advanced technologies.

Central heating may be a good option for your house if:

- the house is old, large and not very energy efficient;
- the house is made up of many small rooms with no large open areas;
- there is no suitable place to install a fireplace or wood stove;
- fire viewing is not a high priority; or
- you wish to confine wood fuel to the basement area.

The increased popularity of in-floor radiant heating with a network of pipes installed below the floor surface has led to an increase in the use of wood-fired boilers. Both indoor and outdoor boilers have been used for this purpose. One big advantage of boilers is that they can readily be used to heat domestic wash water, as well as provide heating for the house.

Wood furnaces and boilers can be installed to work in conjunction with systems using other fuels such as oil, natural gas and electricity. Combination wood–oil or wood–electric furnaces can use both energy sources in a single–packaged unit. Add-on furnaces and boilers can be installed beside existing furnaces and boilers using other fuels. All such units must be safety tested and certified for this purpose.

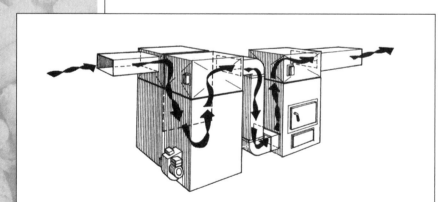

The add-on is placed beside the existing furnace and special ducts are installed to connect the two units. Note that the air passes through the original furnace, then through the add-on and into the ducts for distribution to the house.

Outdoor Boilers

Looking like metal garden sheds with short chimneys, outdoor boilers have gained popularity in rural Canada. Outdoor boilers are usually constructed with a large firebox surrounded by a water jacket, and can be located up to 40 m (130 ft.) from the house or building they heat. Heated water is pumped through an insulated underground pipe to a heat exchanger where heat is transferred to the building. A second pipe returns the cooled water to the boiler to be reheated. These pipes must be carefully insulated or much of the heat will be lost to the ground.

Outdoor boilers appeal to people in rural areas because of their ability to heat a house, its domestic wash water and, if necessary, another building such as a workshop. Other features considered desirable are their location outside the house and the idea that larger pieces of less processed firewood could be used. However, problems arose because the simple fireboxes of almost all brands could not burn the wood effectively. The result was large plumes of smoke and efficiency as low as 40 per cent. The smoking problem is so serious that many municipalities across Canada have restricted the locations where outdoor boilers can be installed.

In response to the problems, an emission test standard was recently developed and advanced-technology outdoor boilers are becoming available. If you are considering an outdoor boiler, choose an advanced-technology model, one with low smoke emissions and high efficiency. Also, by burning only clean, seasoned firewood you will improve efficiency and reduce the smoke emissions from your boiler. An outdoor boiler installation is costly so protect your investment by getting good advice and the services of an experienced installer.

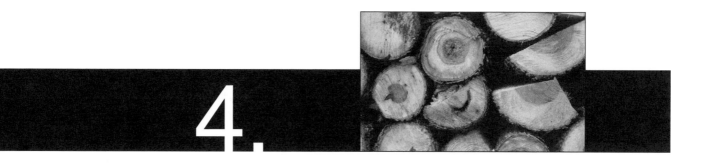

4.

PLANNING A SPACE HEATER INSTALLATION

If you want a wood-burning space heater to make a contribution to your home's total heating needs, some planning should be done before selecting the appliance and deciding on a location.

If you want a wood-burning space heater to make a contribution to your home's total heating needs, some planning should be done before selecting the appliance and deciding on a location. Whether you choose a wood stove, high-efficiency factory-built fireplace, masonry heater, fireplace insert or pellet stove, the same issues should be considered.

Put it Where You Live

Choosing the right location for the space heater may be the most important decision you make. The heater should be located in the part of the house you want to be the warmest. This is usually the main floor area where kitchen, living and dining rooms are located and where families normally spend most of their time. By locating the space heater in this area, you will be warm and comfortable while you eat meals and relax in the evenings.

Avoid Putting It in the Basement

A basement location is not usually good for effective space heating. Although the heated air from the stove does rise to higher levels of the house, it does not do so very effectively. Usually, in an effort to keep the main floor living spaces comfortably warm, the basement is overheated. This wastes fuel and the constant high firing can damage the stove. Unfinished basements are particularly bad locations because much of the heat is absorbed by the poorly insulated walls and floor and lost to the outside. Also, space heaters operating in basements are often unattended and may over-fire or smoulder without anyone noticing. The basement is only a good location for a space heater if your family spends much of its time in a basement family or recreation room. If you do decide to install a wood-burning appliance in the basement, it is important that the chimney be installed up through the house interior rather than through the wall and up the outside.

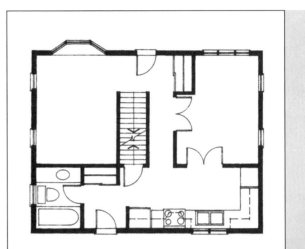

A house like this, with spaces divided by walls, can be difficult to heat with a single space heater. A central heating furnace might be a better choice.

Houses with an open plan design, where there are few walls to separate rooms on the main floor, can usually be heated effectively with a space heater.

Balancing Appliance Output and Room Size

The layout of your house can affect the selection of the right appliance. If the main floor is divided by walls into small rooms, you will probably not be able to heat it entirely with a single space heater. Even a small stove can make a confined space uncomfortably warm. Houses with small rooms are more effectively heated by a central heating furnace or boiler.

Houses of open plan design with few separations between rooms can often be heated completely with a space heater. Because the heat can flow easily to different areas, a larger space heater can be used without causing overheating. An experienced wood heat retailer is usually your best source of advice on appliance sizing for your home. When you visit a retail store to look over the available options, take along the blueprints or a floor plan of your house. This will save time and help the salesperson give you better advice.

Consider the Chimney Location

As you will learn later in this book, the chimney type, location and arrangement has a lot to do with how effectively your space heating system will function. When planning the location for the appliance, consider where the chimney can be routed. Most importantly, avoid running the chimney up the outside wall of the house. Wood burning appliances always work best when they are connected to chimneys that run straight up through the house interior.

Distributing Heat from the Space Heater

For efficient and comfortable space heating, heat must be able to flow from one area of the house to another. Distributing heat from a space heater can be easy or difficult depending on the house layout and the details of its construction. For example, energy-efficient houses with open plans are easier to heat with one stove or fireplace because they lose heat slowly, even from bedrooms that are distant from the heater. A small amount of heat can keep rooms comfortable. Leaky houses are the opposite. Remote rooms get cold quickly and may not be warmed by a stove located down the hall in the living room.

Whether or not the appliance has an internal fan, the heat from a space heater eventually rises to ceiling level. This rising flow of warm air creates a convection current in which warm air moves across the ceiling to walls then falls to floor level where it is drawn back towards the space heater to be reheated. Heat collecting at ceiling level also tends to flow slowly up through open stair wells to higher levels of the home. These convection currents of warm air develop slowly, so you cannot expect them to be effective in distributing heat if the space heater is not kept operating continuously.

Here are some options for assisting natural convection in distributing heat.

■ If the room containing the stove has a high ceiling, a ceiling fan can move the heated air back down into the living space. This slow circulation of air will improve the overall efficiency of the installation.

■ The wall area above interior doors blocks the flow of ceiling-level warm air into hallways and nearby rooms. The drywall or other sheathing in this area can be removed to provide a path for warm air to flow into adjacent areas. In some cases this increased flow can make a big difference and it has the advantage of using no electricity.

■ Small fans that fit in the top corner of a doorway can help to move heat. These are available from wood heat dealers and some hardware stores.

■ The air circulating fan of a central heating furnace can be used to move air around the house. By operating the furnace fan on low speed, the air is gradually mixed and distributed throughout the house. If you are planning to build a new home, you could consider having your heating contractor install cold air return grilles

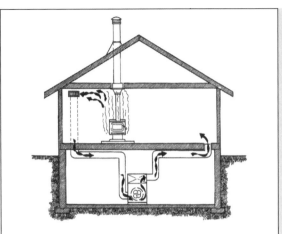

A central furnace fan operating on low speed can slowly circulate the air in the house and distribute the heat from the stove to other areas. Used continuously, this approach causes increased electrical consumption for the house.

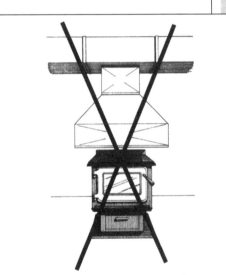

CAUTION Never attempt to use a wood stove as a central furnace by putting a hood over it and connecting a furnace duct to the hood. This practice not only violates the building codes, it also disrupts the air-moving system and can cause the stove to spill smoke into the room. The biggest danger is the possible reversal of chimney flow that can quickly fill the house with carbon monoxide which can be hazardous.

on the wall at ceiling level in the room where the heater is to be located. Since the heated air from the stove will rise to the ceiling, the grilles don't need to be close to the stove to pick up the heated air and circulate it around the house. It is important, however, that the flow of air into and out of the room through the ducts and registers is balanced. The disadvantage of using a furnace fan continuously is the increased consumption of electricity. If you decide to distribute heat by continuous use of your furnace circulating fan, a high-efficiency fan motor can make a big difference in electricity use. When upgrading your furnace, look for one with a good motor that can circulate house air using 100 watts of power or less.

- Grilles in walls and floors can provide a path for the flow of warm air. Note that such grilles need to be large in area to be effective and they reduce privacy and noise control between rooms.

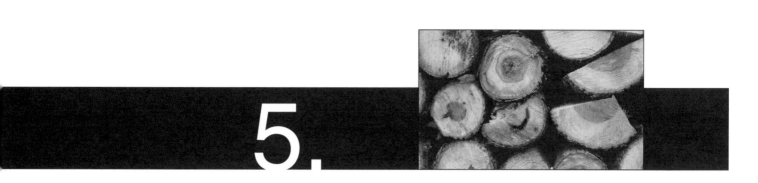

5.

INSTALLATION SAFETY

A serious effort to improve the safety record of residential wood burning has been ongoing since 1980. Before that time stoves were not tested for safety and homeowners had little or no guidance on installation.

A serious effort to improve the safety record of residential wood burning has been ongoing since 1980. Before that time stoves were not tested for safety and homeowners had little or no guidance on installation. The result was many house fires. Today, after many years of cooperative effort by all levels of government and the wood heating industry, a number of systems have been put in place to help you heat with wood safely. These safety measures include:

- A reliable installation code was developed— CSA Standard B365.

- Safety testing standards for stoves, inserts, fireplaces, furnaces, chimneys and flue pipes were developed. Now almost all of the equipment offered for sale carries a certification label indicating that it conforms to safety tests.

- A training program for retailers, installers, chimney sweeps, municipal fire and building inspectors, and insurance inspectors was created. There are now professionals in every part of Canada who have completed the courses of the Wood Energy Technical Training (WETT) program. WETT issues certificates of qualification to successful students.

Wood heating technology and its safe installation have become more complicated in recent years. No longer is it sensible to simply "hook up" a wood stove to an existing chimney and begin using it for heating. To get the best performance from a wood-burning system and to be assured of its safety, you should get reliable advice from a trained professional and consider having the system professionally installed. Before starting the installation you should contact your municipal office to get a building permit and inform your insurance agent of your intentions.

Wood Energy Technical Training

Look for this symbol as your assurance of reliable information, advice and services.

The Wood Energy Technical Training program (WETT) is a series of courses during which wood heat professionals, such as installers, chimney sweeps, retailers and inspectors, learn the details of the installation codes and proper installation, maintenance and inspection procedures. Graduates of the program are issued wall certificates and wallet cards and are allowed to display the WETT logo in their stores, on their service vehicles and in advertising materials. Note that WETT does not certify businesses, but only the individuals who pass their courses and have adequate field experience. When seeking information, advice and installation or maintenance services you can rely on, look for the WETT logo. A wood-heating installation is worth getting it right the first time. Your effort will pay off in comfort and peace of mind in the years to come.

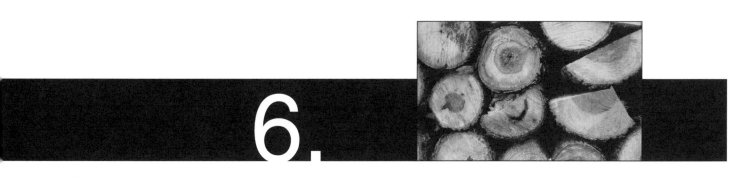

6.

THE INSTALLATION OF WOOD STOVES

This section on the installation of wood stoves gives more detail than is provided on the other categories of wood heating equipment.

This section on the installation of wood stoves gives more detail than is provided on the other categories of wood-heating equipment. There are two reasons for this extra detail. First, wood stoves are the most common type of wood burning equipment in Canada, accounting for more than half of all wood heating equipment. Second, many householders choose to install and maintain their own wood stoves. The information provided here is not complete, but is provided as a general safety guide. If you intend to install your own wood stove, first get advice from a wood heat dealer whose staff is trained and certified under the WETT program. Have the system inspected by someone who is WETT-certified after the work is complete.

Maintaining Safe Clearances to Combustible Material

Combustible materials in walls, floors and ceilings must be protected from the heat from wood burning systems. Protection can be in the form of a minimum distance from combustibles or in the form of shielding that blocks the heat from reaching combustibles.

The installation guidelines for wood stoves can be grouped into two categories. The first is stoves that have been tested and certified as meeting safety standards. The tests determine minimum installation clearances and other guidelines. This information is found in the manufacturer's installation instructions. All new wood stoves currently offered for sale in Canada have been safety certified and most insurance companies will only accept certified appliances.

The second group is those appliances that are not tested and certified. These include used or antique stoves or stoves built before about 1980. There are several good reasons to avoid using uncertified stoves.

■ They are less efficient than safety certified, advanced-technology stoves and they produce a lot more air pollution.

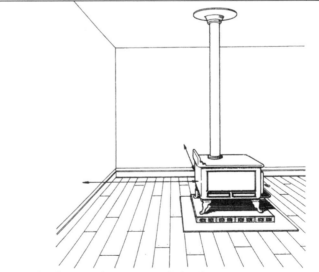

The clearance for an uncertified radiant stove is 1200 mm (48 in.) and for a stove with a sheet metal jacket or casing the clearance is 900 mm (36 in.). The clearances are large because they apply to all shapes, sizes and designs of stoves that have not been tested to determine the actual clearances.

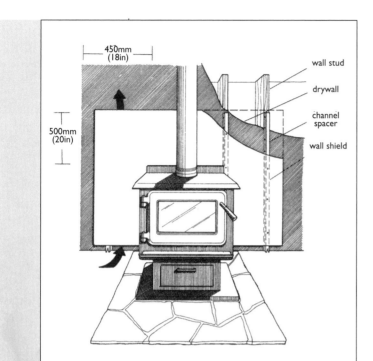

450mm
(18in)

500mm
(20in)

wall stud

drywall

channel
spacer

wall shield

By allowing air to flow between the shield and the combustible surface, a wall shielding assembly can be used to safely reduce minimum clearances. Note that the bottom of the channel spacer is notched to allow cool air to enter.

- Their installation rules are much more complicated and their installation clearances are much larger. The minimum clearances to combustible materials for uncertified appliances are quite large — 1200 mm (48 in.) to the sides and rear of radiant stoves and 900 mm (36 in.) for stoves surrounded by jackets behind which convection air can flow.

- Uncertified stoves are often less attractive and more difficult to use.

- Many insurance companies will not provide coverage to houses that have uncertified stoves installed.

Guidelines for the installation of these uncertified stoves are found in the CSA solid fuel installation code, CSA B365. If you decide to install an uncertified stove, such as an antique cooking range, get assistance from a qualified wood heating dealer, installer or chimney sweep.

Reducing Minimum Clearances Safely

Most homeowners want their wood stove installation to take up as little floor space as possible. Even though the clearances for safety certified stoves are small, it is possible to reduce them further using special shields. The clearances for both certified and uncertified stoves can be reduced safely using the rules set out in CSA standard B365. The common feature of the clearance reduction rules provided in B365 is the air space between the shield material and the wall or ceiling. This space sets up a convection flow of air as the stove is operating and prevents the stove's heat from reaching the surface behind it. The percentage in Table 4 is the amount that the minimum clearance may be reduced with the particular shield system that is described. Both wall and ceiling clearances may be reduced using shields.

A variety of materials can be used for clearance-reducing shields, from simple sheet metal to more decorative shields using brick, stone slices or ceramic tiles. Shields must be permanently mounted to walls or ceilings. Free-standing, folding panels are not acceptable as clearance-reducing shields.

Safety tested and labelled shields are also available for the reduction of minimum clearances. These shields are put through a series of tests to determine how well they can reduce clearances. They are certified and carry a label that confirms they have passed the tests and gives clearance reduction details. Some of these commercial shields are designed so that they can be attached directly to combustible walls without the need for an air space.

The first step in reducing clearances is to determine the minimum clearance from the appliance label or stove installation instructions. Then, calculate the allowed clearance reduction for the type of shield you plan to use from the table on clearance reduction.

Table 4

TYPE OF PROTECTION (SHIELD)	CLEARANCES MAY BE REDUCED BY THESE PERCENTAGES	
	SIDES AND REAR %	TOP %
Sheet metal, a minimum of 29 gauge in thickness, spaced out at least 21 mm (7/8 in) by noncombustible spacers	67	50
Ceramic tiles, or equivalent noncombustible material, on noncombustible supports spaced out at least 21 mm (7/8 in) by noncombustible spacers	50	33
Ceramic tiles, or equivalent noncombustible material, on noncombustible supports, with a minimum of 29 gauge sheet metal backing spaced out at least 21 mm (7/8 in) by noncombustible spacers	67	50
Brick, spaced out at least 21 mm (7/8 in) by noncombustible spacers	50	N/A
Brick, with a minimum of 29 gauge sheet metal backing, spaced out at least 21 mm (7/8 in) by noncombustible spacers	67	N/A

Reducing Clearances with Shielding

Source: CSA Standard B365, Table 3 "Reduction in Appliance and Ductwork Clearance from Combustible Material with Specified Forms of Protection"

Shield Construction Rules

1) Minimum space between shield and combustibles: 21 mm (7/8 in.).

2) Minimum clearance along the bottom of shield: 25 mm (1 in.).

3) Maximum clearance along the bottom of shield: 75 mm (3 in.).

4) Minimum clearance along the top of shield at ceiling: 75 mm (3 in.).

5) Shield extension beyond each side of appliance: 450 mm (18 in.).

6) Shield extension above appliance: 500 mm (20 in.).

7) Edge clearance for ceiling shields: 75 mm (3 in.).

8) Adhesives used in shield construction must not ignite or lose adhesive qualities at temperatures likely to be encountered.

9) Mounting hardware must allow full vertical ventilation.

10) Mounting hardware must not be located closer than 200 mm (8 in.) from the vertical centre line of the appliance.

11) Mounting hardware that extends from the shield surface into combustibles may be used only at the lateral extremities of the shield.

The channel spacers (page 31) shown are the most effective type to use because they give good support to the shield and do not transmit heat through the mounting hardware to the combustible wall. Metal wall strapping, available from most building supply stores, is made of light steel channels that work well as shield spacers. The shield must extend 450 mm (18 in.) beyond each edge of the appliance and 500 mm (20 in.) above the top of the appliance. When the stove clearance is reduced by the use of a suitable shield, flue pipe clearances must still comply with the rules listed in the flue pipe section.

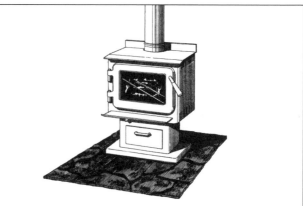

The floor pad protects flooring from hot embers that might fall from the appliance during fuel loading or servicing. The pad must extend at least 200 mm (8 in.) beyond the sides and rear and 450 mm (18 in.) in front of the loading door(s). The floor pad must be a continuous, non-combustible surface.

Protection for the Floor

Safety certified wood stoves will not overheat combustible floors. During testing, the floor temperature is checked and must not exceed safe limits. Although the floor will not overheat due to stove operation, it must be protected from live embers that might fall from the stove during fire tending or ash removal, so a floor pad is needed. The floor pad must be made of a durable, non-combustible material, such as sheet metal, grouted ceramic tile, or mortared brick. Floor pads must normally extend not less than 450 mm (18 in.) in front of the loading door and 200 mm (8 in.) beyond the other sides and back. Floor pads must not be installed on carpet unless the pad is structurally supported so that it does not move, crack or distort.

Uncertified stoves have not passed safety tests, so heat from the bottom may overheat floors. The rules for floor protection for uncertified stoves are complicated, with several different types depending on how high the legs support the stove from the floor. If you are installing an uncertified stove, you should contact a qualified professional for details.

The Safe Installation of Flue Pipes

Flue pipes carry the exhaust gases from the stove (or furnace or boiler) flue collar to the base of the chimney. They have been referred to as the "weak link" in the wood-burning system because they are too often installed improperly. There are two common problems with flue pipe installations. One is that they are often installed too close to combustible material and the other is that sometimes they are not securely fastened and can come apart when put under stress. If your wood-heating appliance has a single wall flue pipe assembly, make sure it is installed exactly according to the list of safety rules provided here.

Flue pipe assemblies should be as short and direct as possible between the stove and the entrance to the chimney. The ideal assembly is one that rises straight up from the stove flue collar and directly into the chimney with no elbows. A straight flue pipe assembly offers the least restriction to gas flow and results in stronger draft. Straight assemblies also need less maintenance because there are no horizontal sections where creosote deposits can build up.

Certified double-wall flue pipe systems are tested to determine the minimum clearance at which they can be installed. The clearance information is found on the labels attached to the pipe and in the manufacturer's installation instructions. The labels on flue pipe should not be removed because they are the proof that the pipe is certified for the purpose.

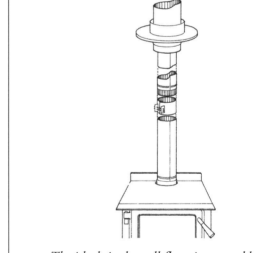

The ideal single-wall flue pipe assembly runs straight up from the stove. Straight venting systems produce stronger draft and will need less maintenance than if the assembly has elbows. A straight single-wall flue pipe assembly needs an inspection sleeve or telescopic section so it can be installed and removed without having to move the appliance. The sleeve also allows some movement for expansion when the flue pipe gets hot.

Rules for Single-Wall Flue Pipe Assemblies

- Minimum clearance from combustible material: 450 mm (18 in.).

- The minimum clearance may be reduced by 50 per cent to 225 mm (9 in.) if suitable shielding is installed either on the pipe or on the combustible surface.

- Maximum overall length of straight pipe: 3 m (10 ft.).

- Maximum unsupported horizontal length: 1 m (3 ft.).

- Maximum number of 90 degree elbows: 2

- Minimum upward slope towards the chimney: 20 mm/m (1/4 in/ft.).

- The crimped ends (male) of the sections must be oriented towards the appliance.

- Each joint in the assembly must be fastened with at least three screws, including the connections at the appliance flue collar and chimney.

- 6, 7, and 8 in. diameter flue pipes must be at least 24 gauge in thickness.

- Galvanized flue pipes must not be used because the coatings vaporize at high temperatures and release dangerous gases. Use black painted flue pipes.

- The assembly must have allowance for expansion. Elbows in assemblies allow for expansion. Straight assemblies should include an inspection sleeve with one end unfastened, or a telescopic section.

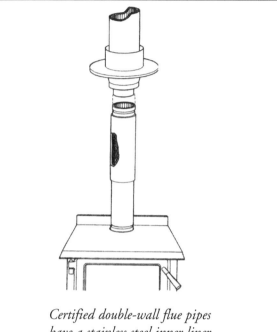

Certified double-wall flue pipes have a stainless steel inner liner and a sealed or vented outer shell. These pipes cost more than single-wall pipe, but last longer and produce a more stable assembly. Double-wall pipes can normally be placed much closer to combustible materials than single-wall pipe.

The rules for their installation are different than the rules for single-wall flue pipe, especially installation clearances which are much less than those for single-wall pipe. Also, the maximum length of a double-wall flue pipe assembly may be greater than is permitted for single-wall pipe.

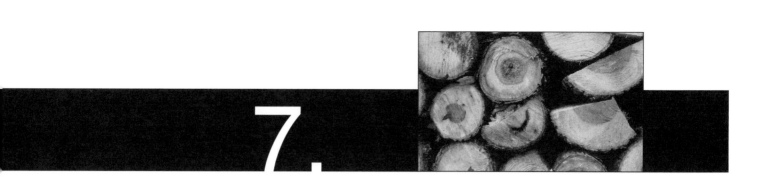

7.

THE INSTALLATION OF OTHER WOOD HEATING SYSTEMS

One general rule that applies to the installation of all fireplace inserts is that there must be a full stainless steel chimney liner installed from the insert flue collar to the top of the chimney.

The Installation of Fireplace Inserts and Hearthmount Stoves

One general rule that applies to the installation of all fireplace inserts is that there must be a full stainless steel chimney liner installed from the insert flue collar to the top of the chimney. The liner matches the flue to the size of the insert collar and isolates the flue gas from the masonry structure, retaining its heat and producing stronger draft. The liner also makes cleaning and servicing easier since it can be cleaned from the top of the chimney and the deposits can be removed from inside the insert. A full liner makes it unnecessary to remove the insert for cleaning, a procedure that is costly and can damage the hearth.

You should be aware that the installation of a fireplace insert or hearthmount stove and its chimney liner is a permanent installation. The structure of the masonry fireplace must be altered to complete the installation and it may not be possible to return it to its original condition if you change your mind later.

When an insert or hearthmount is installed in a fireplace, it is often necessary to extend the hearth to provide protection for the floor so that it is at least 450 mm (18 in.) beyond the front of the appliance. This hearth extension must be permanently mounted to the floor. Hearth rugs are not considered adequate floor protection.

While the installation of a fireplace insert may appear simple, it is not a do-it-yourself job. The existing fireplace and chimney must be cleaned thoroughly so that no creosote remains. The liner installation can be tricky and the correct materials must be used. Since modern inserts are intended for permanent installation and should not need removal for cleaning, you want to be sure that the connections are secure and that all materials used are corrosion-resistant. Professional installers know the potential trouble spots and how to avoid future problems.

The Installation of Advanced Factory-built Fireplaces

Because these fireplaces are installed against and enclosed by combustible building materials, great care must be taken during installation. The fireplace, its heating ducts, chimney, and other components are safety tested together as a unit. There are no general installation instructions for factory-built fireplaces; each one has its own distinct installation rules contained in the manufacturer's installation manual. The manual is checked and approved as part of the certification process. The only assurance you have that the fireplace will operate reliably and safely for many years to come is to make sure

that it is installed exactly according to the manufacturer's instructions. The installation of advanced factory-built fireplaces is not a do-it-yourself job. For a safe and effective system, use the services of trained professionals for the installation.

The Installation of Masonry Heaters

Masonry heaters are entirely different in design, construction and operation than conventional masonry fireplaces. The core of the heater, consisting of the firebox and heat exchanger, is made up of firebrick and a number of precast components made of high-temperature masonry materials. These are assembled by the heater mason and surrounded by the finish material, either brick or stone. The mason must be experienced in the construction of masonry heaters because simple errors can result in the failure of the heater in a short period of time. The clearances of a masonry heater to combustible construction must meet the requirements found in building codes for conventional fireplaces. The Masonry Heater Association of North America manages a heater-mason training and certification program. Your best assurance of an effective and durable unit is to have it designed and built by an MHA-certified heater mason.

The Installation of Pellet-burning Appliances

The installation guidelines for pellet-burning appliances are contained in the manufacturer's certified installation instructions. The instruction manual will provide details for clearances, the materials to be used for venting of the exhaust and the arrangement of vent components. Although some pellet appliances can be installed with through-the-wall vents, experience has shown that they operate more reliably when the venting system includes vertical rise. Ask the pellet appliance dealer about the correct venting arrangement.

Pellet stoves use an internal fan to draw in combustion air and to force the exhaust into the venting system. As a result, pellet-appliance venting systems often operate under positive pressure, so each joint must be sealed carefully to prevent leakage of exhaust into the house. Flue pipe, whether single or double wall, is never used in pellet stove installations.

To operate correctly, the pellet appliance must be connected to a proper venting system and the combustion fan and auger must be adjusted to burn the pellets correctly. Your best assurance of a successful installation is to have it done by an experienced professional.

The Installation of Central Heating Furnaces and Boilers

When considering central heating with wood, your heating retailer or contractor is your best source of information on available systems and their suitability for your home. Since the installation of central heating appliances is complex and requires several specialized skills, it is recommended that you hire professionals to do the work. All wood-burning furnaces and boilers must be certified as meeting a safety standard. During testing, the details of installation are determined. As a result, the installation rules for each central heating furnace or boiler can be different and will be found in the manufacturer's installation instructions. Also, installation is complicated and should be carried out by a trained professional. For these reasons, no details can be offered in this book on how these units should be installed.

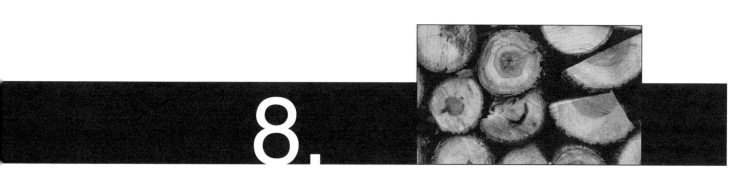

8.

THE CHIMNEY

An effective chimney is an important part of any successful wood-burning system.

How Chimneys Work

An effective chimney is an important part of any successful wood-burning system. Many of the complaints about poor performance of wood-burning systems are traced to chimney problems of various kinds. Knowing how chimneys work is not only necessary in selecting the correct chimney and designing the installation, but is useful in the day-to-day operation of the system.

> Modern, efficient appliances need modern, efficient chimneys. The selection, location and installation of the chimney is at least as important as the type of wood-burning appliance you choose. A properly designed and installed chimney will give many years of reliable service and will allow your appliance to perform properly.

Chimneys operate on the principle that hot air rises. The hot gas in a chimney tends to rise because it is less dense than the cold air outside the house. The rising hot gas creates a pressure difference called draft which draws combustion air into the appliance and expels the exhaust gas outdoors. The hotter the gas compared to the outdoor air, the stronger the draft.

The chimney's function is to produce the draft that draws combustion air into the appliance and safely release the exhaust gases to the outdoors. To fulfil this role, the chimney must:

- Isolate nearby combustible materials from flue gas heat.

- Conserve flue gas heat to produce strong draft.

- Be resistant to corrosion on the inside and to weather effects on the outside.

- Be sealed to prevent leakage.

- Tolerate the high gas temperatures that can result from chimney fires.

Here are some guidelines for effective chimney installations. Some are code requirements, others are recommended for good chimney performance:

- Building codes require that the top of the chimney extend not less than 1 m (3 ft.) above the point it exits the roof, and 60 cm (2 ft.) higher than any roof, building or other obstacle within a horizontal distance of 3 m (10 ft.). These rules are intended to place the top of the chimney higher than any areas of air turbulence caused by wind. In practice, chimneys must sometimes be higher than this to clear air turbulence caused by nearby obstacles.

- **The chimney should be installed up through the house rather than out through a wall and up the outside.** When chimneys run up outside walls, they are exposed to the outside cold and this chilling effect can reduce the available draft at the appliance. Even worse, outside chimneys create cold backdrafts when the appliance is not in use, particularly if it is a basement installation. A

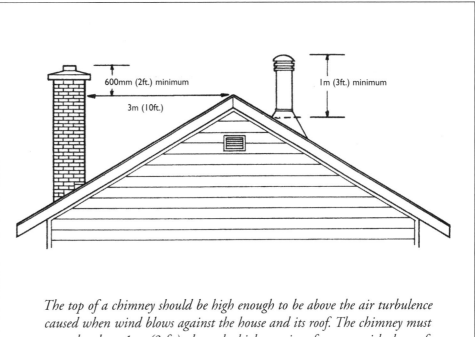

The top of a chimney should be high enough to be above the air turbulence caused when wind blows against the house and its roof. The chimney must extend at least 1 m (3 ft.) above the highest point of contact with the roof, and at least 60 cm (2 ft.) higher than any roof line or obstacle within a horizontal distance of 3 m (10 ft.).

backdraft allows cold air and odours to flow down the chimney, through the appliance and into the room. A backdrafting chimney also makes it hard to build a fire without getting smoke in the house. Chimneys that run up through the house benefit from being enclosed within the warm house environment. Inside chimneys produce stronger, more reliable draft and do not cold backdraft.

■ Keeping flue gases hot is the best way to produce reliable chimney draft. If you experience problems such as sluggish draft or smoking when you open the loading door to add fuel, low flue gas temperature may be the problem. You can increase chimney temperature by building smaller, hotter fires made with smaller pieces of wood. A 90 degree elbow in a flue pipe assembly may be replaced with two 45 degree elbows to reduce the horizontal run and improve flow. If your chimney is made of brick, you could have a stainless steel liner installed. The new liner will improve draft by keeping the flue gases hotter as they rise in the chimney.

■ Taller chimneys usually produce stronger draft. A rule of thumb for minimum height states that the total system height (from the floor the appliance is mounted on to the top of the chimney) should never be less than 4.6 m (15 ft.). Most normal installations exceed this height, but installations in cottages with shallow-pitch roofs may not. If draft problems are experienced with a short system, consider adding to the chimney height. However, if draft problems are experienced with systems higher than the recommended minimum system height, adding to the chimney may have little or no effect.

■ The chimney flue should be the same size as the appliance flue collar. Over-sized chimneys were common in the past, partly because people used to think that bigger is better. Now it is clear that bigger is not better when it comes to chimney sizing. A given volume of flue gas flows faster and has less time to lose heat in a small chimney flue than in a large one. In planning wood heating systems, experienced installers will sometimes choose a chimney that has a smaller inside diameter than the appliance flue collar. This is usually done when the chimney runs straight up inside the house and is very tall. Chimneys that are more than 8 m (about 25 ft.) in height sometimes produce more draft than the appliance needs, so a smaller chimney can be used without any reduction in performance. The decision as to whether the flue size may be reduced from that of the appliance flue collar must be left to an experienced technician.

Suitable Chimney Options

There are two general types of chimneys that are approved for use with wood-burning appliances:

Factory-built metal chimneys of particular types may be used with wood-burning appliances. Wood stoves, central heating furnaces and some factory-built fireplaces must use the 650°C (1,200°F) metal chimney. The continuous gas temperature it is designed for is higher than for chimneys intended for other fuels. Most factory-built fireplaces are also approved for use with a special chimney that has the same upgraded liner found in the 650°C type. Your wood heat retailer can show you the differences between these types and which one you will need to use for your installation. All factory-built chimneys must be installed exactly according to the manufacturer's instructions and only certified components should be used.

Masonry chimneys that are built according to the rules found in building codes may be used with wood-burning appliances. These chimneys have a clay tile liner surrounded by a brick or stone shell. If you are planning to have a masonry chimney built, be sure to get a building permit and make sure the mason who builds it knows and follows the code rules. Insulated stainless steel liners can be used as an alternative to clay liners in new masonry chimneys to reduce heat loss and improve performance.

If you see any deterioration of the bricks or mortar joints near the top of the chimney, or if there are dark stains on the brick work, you should have the chimney inspected immediately. Hire a chimney sweep certified under the WETT program to clean and inspect the chimney. Masonry chimneys that have been damaged by a chimney fire or are too large for the appliance you want to connect can be relined with a certified stainless steel liner. These liners can be of either rigid or corrugated flex design.

Unsuitable Chimneys

Type A Chimneys are an older type of metal chimney used before 1981 and are not considered suitable for wood-burning appliances. Type A chimneys were originally designed for oil furnaces and are unable to withstand the high temperatures of a chimney fire. If your chimney has a painted exterior or if the outside casing is square, it could be a Type A. If you have a Type A chimney, upgrade it to the new 650°C chimney as soon as possible. Deteriorated metal chimneys can be hazardous.

Bracket masonry chimneys are not supported on proper concrete foundations and should not be used. Bracket chimneys are brick chimneys built on wooden supports within a wall of the house. They are common in older houses, particularly in rural areas. Bracket chimneys cannot be upgraded to meet current building code requirements and should be replaced.

Unlined masonry chimneys should not be used because all masonry chimneys must have a liner made of clay tiles, firebrick or stainless steel to be considered suitable. In some cases old, unlined chimneys can be upgraded by the installation of a certified stainless steel liner.

Air-cooled chimneys are used for some decorative factory-built fireplaces. Air-cooled chimneys use a flow of air between inner and outer layers to keep the outer surface cool. Wood-burning heating appliances, such as stoves and furnaces, should never be connected to air-cooled chimneys.

Creosote and Chimney Fires

Wood smoke can condense on the cool inner surface of a chimney, producing a build up of creosote deposits. Creosote is a highly-flammable material and if it ignites at the base of the chimney, it can produce a raging fire that travels up the chimney causing extremely high temperatures as it spreads. The high temperature can damage the clay liners in a masonry chimney or the metal liner in a factory-built chimney. Although 650°C chimneys can withstand chimney fire temperatures, the heat still causes extreme stress in the chimney.

Chimney fires are the result of poor appliance firing techniques combined with a lack of proper chimney maintenance. When wood-burning appliances are operated properly using the techniques outlined later in this book, some creosote may still be deposited, but it will be of a less combustible type. Instead of the black, tarry type of creosote that results from smouldering fires, the creosote that results from proper firing is soft, flaky or powdered.

Chimney fires can be prevented. Your chimney should be checked for deposits regularly until you know how quickly creosote builds up. Older, conventional wood stoves and furnaces can produce creosote quickly because they are unable to burn the wood as completely as the advanced designs. In severe cases, enough creosote to sustain a damaging chimney fire can be deposited in only a few weeks. The newer, low-emission wood stoves burn the wood so completely that when they are operated properly their chimneys normally need cleaning only once each year.

Never assume that the chimney is clean. Check it regularly to be certain, especially during the spring and fall. If you do have a chimney fire, have the chimney inspected and repaired if necessary before using the system again.

Preventing Smoke, Smells and Cold Hearths

The spicy smell of wood smoke in the air on a cold winter evening can be pleasant. But the smell of wood smoke inside your home is a sign that the wood-burning system is not functioning properly. The smoke contains harmful air pollutants that can be irritating or even dangerous in high concentrations. Properly designed, installed and operated wood-burning systems do not spill smoke into the house. There are three main reasons why some wood-burning systems smoke:

Bad system design: There are design characteristics that can make a wood-burning system more likely to spill smoke. Most of these characteristics result in low flue temperatures and low draft. For example, chimneys that run up the outside wall of the house can rob the heat from the exhaust and produce very little draft. Long flue pipe assemblies allow too much heat to be given up before the gases reach the chimney. Each elbow in the flue pipe assembly slows down the flow of gases and causes a small restriction to flow. When an assembly includes more than one elbow, the restriction can be enough to cause spillage. Any one of these problem characteristics is not usually enough to cause smoke spillage on its own. However, when, for example, an outside chimney is combined with a long flue pipe assembly with several elbows and serves an appliance located in a basement, it is almost certain that smoking will be a problem.

Negative pressure in the house: Canadian houses are more tightly sealed than in the past through the use of better doors and windows and construction techniques. Modern houses are more energy efficient, but are also more sensitive to depressurization when air is exhausted from the house. Where problems arise, the cause is often a powerful kitchen range exhaust.

Because new houses are tightly sealed, there are few holes to allow replacement air to enter, and the house pressure becomes negative compared to atmospheric pressure outside. This negative pressure works against chimney draft and can cause a wood burning appliance to spill smoke, especially when a fire is started or as it dies down to coals. Because it is difficult to predict when or if spillage due to house depressurization will occur, it is important to have a smoke detection and alarm system installed. Such a system includes at least one smoke detector on each level of the house and at least one carbon monoxide detector. The risk of smoke spillage in a house with a large kitchen range exhaust can be eliminated if the exhaust fan is electrically interlocked to a make-up air system that forces air into the home to replace the exhausted air. Contact your wood heat retailer or heating contractor for details.

Improper appliance firing technique: When a wood fire is starved for air it smoulders, producing a relatively cool, smoky fire. The problem usually happens when the air control is turned down too low. During a smouldering fire the temperatures throughout the system are low, meaning that the chimney will not be receiving the hot gas it needs to produce strong draft. Smoke will spill into the room if the appliance loading door is opened as a fire smoulders. A smouldering fire is the single most common reason for smoke spillage. By using the suggestions on proper firing technique later in this book, you will be able to avoid these smouldering fires.

Does an Outdoor Air Supply Prevent Smoke Spillage?

It has been widely believed that smoke spillage could be reduced or eliminated by supplying outdoor combustion air through a duct, either directly to the appliance firebox or indirectly to the room in which the appliance is installed. However, research shows that outdoor air supplies do not work. When an exhaust fan is running, smoke spillage from an appliance can occur at the same pressure level, whether or not an outdoor air supply is installed. The same research shows that wind effects around the house can reverse the flow in these ducts, drawing air and possibly smoke through the duct to outdoors. This reverse flow can be hazardous if the duct is directly connected to the appliance firebox.

Some building codes still require that outdoor air be supplied to wood-burning fireplaces. You must comply with this rule, but be aware that performance will not improve, and take steps to protect combustible materials around the duct from overheating if the gas flow reverses.

How Chimneys and Houses Interact

The location of the chimney has a big effect on how it functions and on the operation of the wood burning appliance connected to it.

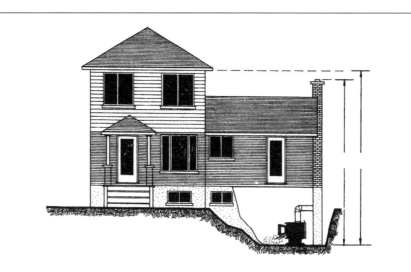

The wood stove in this house will almost certainly have operating problems. Fires will be fussy to light because draft in the system will be weak until the chimney is thoroughly warmed. Smoke may spill from the door when it is opened for loading and there will be some risk of smoke spillage as the fire dies down to a coal bed. Note that the chimney top is lower than the ceiling of the second story, meaning that the house is a higher effective stack than the chimney. The chimney is also located outside the building where it will be cooled. This installation could be improved by moving the appliance and chimney to the wall next to the two-storey section of the house. The chimney would run inside the house up through the second floor and be protected from the cold. It could also be made tall enough to clear the roof of the taller section of the house without being unsightly.

A chimney is an enclosed column of warm air or gases surrounded by colder outside air. The warm air or gas in the chimney is more buoyant than the dense cold outside air so it rises, producing draft in the system.

In winter, your house is also an enclosed column of warm, buoyant air creating a form of "draft." In effect, the rising warm air pushes up towards the top of the house, creating higher air pressure there. At the same time, the pressure in the basement is lower than the pressure outside. That is why the basement of a leaky house feels drafty, as the cold outside air is drawn through leaks into the area of lower pressure, while rooms on the second floor are more comfortable. The difference in pressure at various levels of the house is called **stack effect**. This stack effect can work against upward flow in an outside chimney that serves an appliance installed at the lowest level of a house.

The "Cold-Backdraft-at-Standby"

Many people who heat with wood have experienced this: they go to the basement to build a fire in the wood stove and when they open the door to put in the newspaper and kindling, they can feel cold air. When they light the kindling, the smoke comes into the room instead of up the chimney. This is a cold-backdraft-at-standby. Although this reverse flow can be caused by negative pressure in the house produced by a kitchen range exhaust, it is most often the combined effect of an outside chimney and a basement appliance location.

Here is how it works. When there is no fire in the stove, fireplace or furnace, the air in the chimney cools to the outside temperature and the chimney produces no draft at all. The very slight negative pressure in the basement caused by stack effect in the house is enough to pull the air down the chimney and out through any openings in the stove. The cold air does not fall down the chimney, but is sucked down by stack effect.

Homeowners who have installations like this have found ways to get the fire started without smoke spillage. The usual remedy is to open a basement window or door to neutralize the negative pressure while the fire is lit. Although it does work, this technique only masks the problem, it does not correct it.

If you never want to experience a cold-backdraft-at-standby, don't combine an outside chimney and basement stove location in your installation plans.

Some houses produce more stack effect than others. Two- or three-storey houses produce more stack effect than bungalows because their column of warm air is taller. A house with most of its leaks at the upper levels tends to produce more stack effect because the leaks offer a ready path for warm air to escape—like the open top of a chimney.

Uninsulated, outside chimneys can reverse if the stack effect is strong enough, allowing smoke or cold outside air to spill into the house through the appliance.

Stack effect is always present in houses during cold weather, but its influence can be virtually eliminated by installing the chimney inside the building and routing it so that it exits the house at the top of the highest heated space. Good chimneys—ones that are insulated and run up through the house—are able to overcome the influence of stack effect.

One situation in which the influence of stack effect is most troublesome is where an appliance connected to an outside chimney is installed in the basement of a single-storey addition to a two-story house, as shown in the illustration on page 48. This form of installation should be avoided if possible.

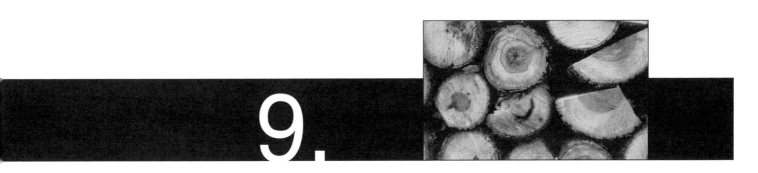

9.

YOUR INSTALLATION CHECKLIST

Before the System is Installed

While the System is Being Installed

After the Installation is Completed

Before the System is Installed:

- Get a permit from your municipal building department. Some municipalities require that you get a building permit just to exchange an older stove for a new one.

- Contact your insurance agent to find out if the installation will affect your premiums. If there will be an increase you think is too high, shop around. Insurance company treatment of wood-heat installations varies widely.

- Spend some time with your retailer, installer or contractor going over the plans for the installation. Make sure you understand what is involved and what the cost will be. If you are installing the unit yourself, get advice from a trained professional on any points for which you need help.

- Read the manufacturer's installation instructions carefully.

While the System is Being Installed:

- Satisfy yourself that the manufacturer's instructions are being followed exactly. If the installer deviates from the instructions, ask why.

After the Installation is Completed:

- Check the installation over to be sure it meets code requirements.

- Have the installation inspected by your municipal building department. Some municipal building and fire departments are reluctant to inspect wood-heat systems. In some cases these departments will refer you to a local WETT-certified retailer, installer or chimney sweep for inspection.

- Notify your insurance agent that the installation is complete.

- Install at least one smoke detector on or near the ceiling at the exit to the room in which the appliance is installed. Replace the batteries annually.

- Install at least one carbon monoxide detector at or near ceiling level.

- Buy a labelled and approved ABC-type fire extinguisher and store it near the installation. Follow the instructions on the extinguisher label for maintenance procedures.

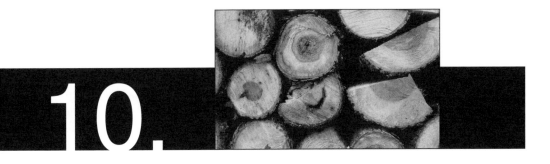

10.

BURNING WOOD EFFICIENTLY

The knowledge and skills needed to operate a wood-burning system properly must be learned and practised to get them right.

The knowledge and skills needed to operate a wood-burning system properly must be learned and practised to get them right. By practising and mastering the techniques offered here, you will reduce the amount of wood you burn to heat your home, reduce smoke pollution outside and inside the house, and increase the convenience and pleasure of burning wood.

The Basics: What Happens When Wood Burns

As firewood burns, it goes through three phases:

> Please Note: The suggestions offered here are general and apply to many appliances used in Canada. However, some combustion systems, notably catalytic systems and masonry heaters, require special firing techniques. Instructions for these techniques will be found in the manufacturer's operation manual. If the manual for the appliance has detailed firing instructions, they should be followed.

Evaporation of water: Up to half the weight of a freshly cut log is water. After proper seasoning the water content is reduced to less than 20 per cent. As the wood is heated in the firebox, this water boils off, consuming heat energy in the process. The wetter the wood, the more heat energy is consumed. That is why wet firewood hisses and sizzles and is hard to burn while properly seasoned wood ignites and burns easily.

The emission of smoke: As the wood heats up above the boiling point of water, it starts to smoke. The smoke is the visible result of the breakdown of the solid wood as it vaporizes into a cloud of combustible gases and tar droplets. The smoke will burn if the temperature is high enough and oxygen is present. When the smoke burns, it produces the bright flames that are characteristic of wood combustion. Smoke that does not burn in the firebox is released into the chimney where it will either condense as creosote deposits or vent to the outdoors as air pollution. Unburned smoke represents an efficiency loss because it contains a large part of the total energy in the wood.

The charcoal phase: As the fire progresses and most of the gases and tars have vaporized out of the wood, charcoal remains. Charcoal is almost entirely carbon and burns with a red glow and very little flame or smoke. Charcoal is a good fuel that burns easily. However, a charcoal fire releases carbon monoxide which is a poisonous gas, so even though it is not smoky, the exhaust must be completely vented to outdoors.

In practice, all three phases of wood combustion can happen at the same time. The wood gases can be flaming and the edges of the pieces can be glowing red as charcoal burns, while water in the core of the piece is still evaporating. The challenge in burning wood effectively is to boil off the water content quickly and make sure the smoke burns with bright flames before it leaves the firebox.

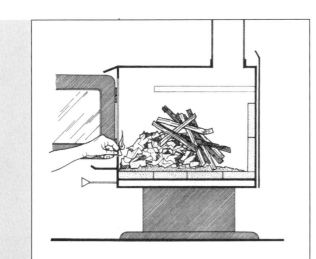

This is the traditional way to start a wood fire. Use plenty of crumpled newspaper and dry, finely-split kindling. Set the air control fully open. Light the newspaper near where the combustion air enters the firebox. When a kindling fire is built properly, you should expect instant ignition and no smouldering.

Starting a New Fire

The first step in building a fire is to find out where the combustion air enters the firebox. For most modern stoves and fireplaces with glass doors, much of the air enters the firebox through a narrow strip above and behind the glass panel. This "air wash" flows down like a curtain to the base of the glass and keeps the tarry smoke from sticking to it. The air reaches the fire at coal bed level. Most older stoves without a glass air-wash system will have an air inlet towards the bottom of the loading door. Whether you have a new stove with glass air-wash or an older stove without it, the front of the firebox, just inside the loading door is normally where you would light the fire so that it gets plenty of air. This location is also the right ignition point for most wood-fired furnaces and boilers.

There are several ways to start a wood fire successfully, and every user develops his or her own method after some trial and error. Regardless of the method you choose, the goal should be a fire that ignites quickly and builds to full intensity without smouldering. For a fire to burn with minimal smoke, its surroundings must be hot, so the first step in a clean burn is to get a hot fire burning to heat up the firebrick and metal parts of the firebox. Here are four ways to build a wood fire: using fire starters, the bottom-up fire, the top-down fire and the in-between fire.

Using fire starters

Fire starters are usually made from a mixture of sawdust and wax, and can be either purchased or homemade. A few small pieces of fire starter are placed among pieces of kindling and then ignited. This is an easy way to light a fire because, as long as enough split kindling pieces are placed close enough to the burning fire starters, the fire will reliably catch. Set the air control to fully open. Depending on the stove design and chimney arrangement, you may need to leave the door open a crack until the fire catches. Since leaving the door open slightly for more than a few minutes can lead to dangerously high temperatures, never leave the stove unattended while starting the fire.

The bottom-up fire

This is the traditional way to build a fire. Crumple as many as 10 sheets of newspaper and put them in the firebox. The amount of newspaper you need will depend on the firebox size, and the dryness and fineness of the kindling you are using. The drier and finer the kindling, the less newspaper you need. Many people make the mistake of using too little newspaper. Be generous with the newspaper and you will have more success. Hold the paper down with 10 to 15 pieces of finely split, dry kindling. Softwoods, such as cedar and pine, make good kindling. Ideally, the kindling should be placed on and behind the newspaper so that the combustion air reaches the newspaper first where you light it. It is also a good idea to add two or three very small pieces of firewood to the kindling load before lighting. Set the air control to fully open, light the newspaper and close the door or leave it open a crack.

The disadvantages of the traditional method are that once the paper burns away, the fire can collapse and begin to smoulder, and even if the fire doesn't collapse, it is necessary to open the loading door again once or twice to add larger pieces until a full fire is built.

The top-down fire

The top-down method of building a wood fire is becoming more popular. To build a top-down fire, reverse the traditional method. Place three or four small pieces of split firewood on the floor of the firebox, and put a few pieces of kindling on the logs and some finely split kindling on those. Crumpled sheets of newspaper can be used, but they tend to roll around and fall off the fuel as they burn. A better method is to roll up a full sheet of newspaper from corner to corner and tie a knot in it. Use four or five newspaper knots on and around the kindling. Set the air control to fully open, light the newspaper and close the loading door.

The advantages of the top-down fire building method are minimal start-up smoke, no chance that the fire will collapse and smother itself, and no need to open the loading door to add larger pieces once the kindling fire is established.

The in-between fire

The in-between fire is another common approach. Lay two medium-sized pieces of split firewood on the floor of the firebox. Place some crumpled newspaper between the pieces and lay up to a dozen pieces of finely split kindling across the two logs. When you light the newspaper the kindling catches easily and can't collapse before the two logs catch.

If you have problems getting your fires to start, the cause is likely that either the wood is not split finely enough or it is too wet.

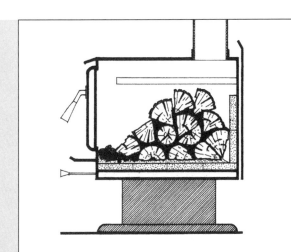

Rake the charcoal towards the front of the stove where the combustion air enters. Place the pieces of wood on and behind the coals. Open the air inlets fully and leave them open until the pieces of wood are well-charred. This illustration shows the arrangement of pieces for an extended fire.

Rekindling a Fire from Charcoal

For most wood-burning appliances, the live coals that remain after the fire has burned down are found at the back of the firebox furthest from the air supply. This is the time to clear excess ash from the firebox. Before disturbing the remaining charcoal, remove a small amount of ash from the front of the firebox. Now rake the live coals forward to just inside the loading door. If only a small amount of charcoal remains, you will have to start with kindling. If you have a good quantity of glowing charcoal to work with, place at least three, and preferably more than five pieces of firewood on and behind the charcoal. Open the air inlets fully and close the door.

If everything is just right, you should expect instant ignition of the new load. The bottom pieces may start to flame before you get the door closed. Allow the fire to burn until the firebox is full of bright turbulent flames and the wood is charred black. This usually takes between five and 20 minutes, depending on the size of the pieces and the moisture content of the wood. When the wood is charred, you can reduce the air setting to produce the amount of heat and length of burn you desire. If the wood stops flaming, open the air control again and let the fire burn longer until the firebox heats up fully. You may want to try reducing the air control setting in two or three stages. The result will be less smoke because the fire will not have to recover from the single, large reduction in air supply.

The most important rule is: **NEVER LET THE FIRE SMOULDER**. As long as there is solid wood in the firebox, there should be active flames. Without flames the smoke will escape unburned, both reducing efficiency and increasing pollution. With an advanced, medium-sized stove, it is possible to achieve a reliable overnight burn while maintaining flaming combustion and having enough charcoal in the morning to rekindle a new load.

A loosely stacked load is good for short-duration or "flash" fires.

Other Useful Tips

Arranging the firewood: Small pieces of firewood arranged loosely in a criss-cross pattern burn quickly because the heat and combustion air can reach all the pieces at once. Larger pieces placed compactly burn more slowly because there are fewer spaces where the air can penetrate the load. Avoid adding just one or two pieces of wood to a fire at a time. Three or more pieces are needed to form a sheltered pocket of glowing coals that reflect heat toward each other and sustain the fire.

A compact fuel load is good for extended firing cycles

Fire in cycles: Don't expect perfectly steady heat output from a wood fire. Wood fires burn best in cycles. A cycle starts with the ignition of a new load of wood and ends when that load has been reduced to a coal bed. Each cycle should provide between three and eight hours of heating, depending on how much wood was used and how much heat is needed. Plan the firing cycles around your household routine. If someone is home to tend the fire, use a short firing cycle. If you must be away from the house during the day, use the extended firing cycle discussed below.

The flash fire: A flash fire is a small amount of wood burned quickly. Use it in spring and fall when you just want to take the chill off the house. The flash fire technique eliminates the smouldering fires that are common in spring and fall. To build a flash fire, rake the charcoal towards the air inlets and place several small pieces on and behind it. The pieces should be stacked loosely in a crisscross arrangement. Open the air inlet to produce a hot, bright fire. The air supply can be reduced slightly as the fire progresses, but never enough to extinguish the flames. When only charcoal remains, the air supply can be reduced further to prevent cooling the coal bed.

For a flash fire, use a few relatively small pieces of wood to "take the chill off." Load the wood loosely in a crisscross arrangement. Let the fire burn brightly until most of the solid wood is burned before reducing the air setting. Flash fires are effective in spring and fall when the heating load is modest. Using the flash fire technique, you can avoid smoldering fires.

The extended fire: To build a longer-lasting fire, rake the coals towards the air inlets and use larger pieces of wood placed compactly in the firebox. Placing the pieces close together prevents the heat and flame from penetrating the load and saves the buried pieces for later in the burn cycle. Open the air inlets fully for between five to 20 minutes depending on load size and fuel moisture content. When

There are several ways to use or dispose of ashes. They can be spread on icy driveways to provide better traction. Ashes can help to control some garden pests or to reduce soil acidity. Excess wood ashes can be buried in a pit or taken to a rural waste disposal site.

the firebox is full of flames and the outer pieces have a layer of charcoal, reduce the air control in stages to the desired level. The charcoal layer insulates the rest of the wood and slows down the release of combustible gases. This allows you to turn down the air control and still maintain a clean-burning fire. Use the extended fire technique to achieve an overnight burn or a fire to last the day while you are at work. The wood should be actively flaming even after the air setting is reduced for the extended burn.

Removing ashes: When you follow the suggestions for raking of the coal bed before loading, you will find that ashes build up at the front of the firebox. These ashes can be removed easily before coal bed raking in preparation for loading. Most modern wood-burning appliances work best when a small amount of ash is removed often rather than letting it build up for several days.

Many advanced stoves have ash pans below the firebox and various ways to let the ashes fall into them. Some have grates, and others have removable plugs. When these ash removal systems are closed and the stove is operating, no air should leak past the grate or plug. If the coal bed glows at this location, the ash door gasket may need replacing or the ash pan plug may not be fitting properly. These problems should be corrected so the stove can operate as intended.

If your stove does not have an ash pan or if you find the one you have awkward to use, ask your wood stove retailer for an ash handler that you can scoop ashes into through the loading door.

Ashes almost always contain live embers that can stay hot for days and which release carbon monoxide gas. Ashes should be placed in their own metal container with a lid that is stored outside on a surface like concrete. Never store ashes indoors, in a non-metallic container or on a wooden surface like a deck.

Using a thermometer: A stack thermometer was an important indicator of the condition of fires before glass doors with air wash were perfected. With no view of the fire, the thermometer was an important way to know that the wood had ignited properly and wasn't smouldering.

If your appliance doesn't offer a view of the fire, a thermometer might be helpful to you. Every wood-heating system behaves differently and thermometers vary, so it is not possible to give exact temperature guidelines. With some experience you will be able to tell when you have set the air control too low for a long burn and when it is a good time to reload. Install the stack thermometer in the flue pipe about 450 mm (18 in.) above the stove. Some appliance manufacturers recommend the use of a stove-top thermometer rather than a stack thermometer. The function is the same, but the temperature range will be different.

Almost all advanced technology stoves have glass doors with air wash, so you can check the condition of the fire easily without a stack thermometer. If the fire is burning properly the glass might get hazy after a few days of use, but it should not develop large brown stains quickly. If the glass does develop stains quickly, you may be turning the air control down too much, or your wood may be too wet. Brown stains on the glass usually indicates that the fire is burning dirty, which also means creosote deposits can be building up in the chimney. Hearth retailers sell a special cleaner for this ceramic glass.

When you burn wood properly, this is what you should see:

- When wood burns it should be flaming until only charcoal remains. If there are no flames, something is wrong.
- If there are firebricks in the firebox, they should be tan in colour, never black.
- Steel or cast iron parts in the firebox should be light to dark brown, never black and shiny.
- With seasoned wood, correct air settings, and proper loading arrangement, you should expect almost instant ignition of a new load of wood.
- If the appliance has a glass door with air wash, it should be clear.
- If the appliance has a glass door without air wash, it will be hazy, but should never be black.
- The exhaust coming from the top of the chimney should be clear or white. A plume of blue or grey smoke indicates smouldering, poor combustion, air pollution and probably low system operating temperatures.

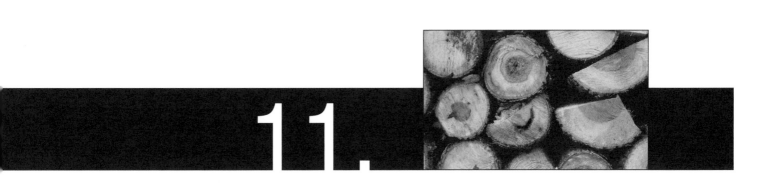

11.
PURCHASING AND PREPARING YOUR FUEL SUPPLY

The quality of the fuel wood you burn can have a big effect on the efficiency and convenience of the system.

The quality of the fuel wood you burn can have a big effect on the efficiency and convenience of the system. The main factors that affect the burning characteristics of firewood are moisture content, tree species and piece size.

When people have trouble with their wood-burning systems, the problem is most often that their wood is not dry enough. When trees are cut, the wood moisture content ranges between 35 and 50 per cent by weight. If you attempt to burn wood this wet, it will be hard to ignite, slow to burn and will hiss and sizzle in the firebox. So much energy will be consumed in boiling of the excess water that the efficiency of combustion will be low. Properly seasoned wood ignites easily and burns efficiently.

Firewood dries slowly and may take a full year or more to season. Very little drying happens before the wood is cut to length, split and stacked. Wood should be stacked in an open area so the pieces can be warmed by the sun and summer breezes can carry away the moisture. Hardwoods like oak and maple dry more slowly than softer woods like spruce and poplar. Large chunks of wood dry more slowly than wood that is split small. Therefore, while finely split soft woods may season adequately in just the summer months, large pieces of hard woods may take up to two years to dry. Properly seasoned wood has a moisture content of less than 20 per cent. There are several ways to tell if firewood is dry enough to burn:

- There are cracks or checks in the end grain.
- The wood darkens with aging from white or cream colour to yellow or grey.
- Bang two pieces together; dry wood sounds hollow, wet wood sounds dull.
- Split a piece and if the fresh surface feels damp and cool, the wood is wet. If it feels dry and warm, it is seasoned.
- Burn some and if it hisses, it is much too wet
- You can test the wood using a moisture meter.

Although the energy content of dry wood per kilogram is almost the same regardless of species, softwoods and hardwoods burn differently because of differences in density. Softwoods, such as pine, spruce and cedar are less dense than hardwoods like oak, maple and beech. Although hardwood trees are plentiful in parts of Canada, there are areas, particularly in the west and north, where softwoods are the main species for fuel wood. Hardwood is usually considered the preferred firewood because it tends to produce a longer-lasting coal bed. However, softwood makes good firewood and is used successfully, even in some of the coldest areas of Canada.

Density of Common Tree Species

Here is a list of the tree species commonly used for firewood. Those at the top of the list are hardest and those at the bottom of the list are the softest.

HARDEST

Ironwood

Rock elm

Hickory

Oak

Sugar maple

Beech

Yellow birch

Ash

Red elm

Red maple

Tamarack

Douglas fir

White birch

Manitoba maple

Red alder

Hemlock

Poplar

Pine

Basswood

Spruce

Balsam

SOFTEST

Even in areas where hardwoods are plentiful, softer species such as poplar can be good fuels for spring and fall use when heat demand is lower. Environmentally friendly woodlot management involves removing some of the dying and damaged trees, and the less desirable species. You can support sustainable forestry practices by accepting fuel that contains a blend of species and being willing to burn the softer woods, such as poplar during spring and fall. The newer advanced-technology stoves, fireplaces and furnaces can burn hardwoods and softwoods equally well.

The size of the firewood pieces affects the way they burn. Larger pieces ignite and release their energy more slowly than small pieces. Smaller pieces are better for short, hot fires and larger pieces are preferable for extended firing cycles. In general, commercial firewood dealers produce firewood in larger pieces than advanced wood-burning appliances can handle. It is often necessary to split some of the wood again before using it. The largest piece size for high-efficiency appliances should not exceed about 150 mm (6 in.) across the largest dimension, and a range of smaller pieces will be needed for effective stoking. At least two or three days supply of wood should be stored indoors. Wood that is brought in from outdoors in winter and loaded into the appliance immediately will cool the fire too much, making it smoky.

Firewood Measurement and Pricing

Firewood is measured and sold in units called cords. A "full" cord measures 1.2 m x 1.2 m x 2.4 m (4 ft. x 4 ft. x 8 ft.) and is the official, standard firewood measure. However, 1.2 m (4 ft.) pieces are never used for home heating. Other terms, such as face cord, stove cord or furnace cord are used to describe a stack of wood measuring 1.2 m (4 ft.) high, 2.4 m (8 ft.) long with a piece length shorter than 1.2 m (4 ft.). The most common firewood piece length is 400 mm (16 in.), or one-third of a full cord, but other lengths are also sold.

The various terms and cord measures can be confusing when you are purchasing firewood. If you want to compare prices from a number of suppliers, take a tape measure to the dealers' yards and measure the average piece length. If the dealer does not price the wood in the standard full cord measure, convert the price to this basic unit. Here are some examples to illustrate the conversion.

Dealer A sells what he calls a "face cord" for $55. You find that the pile is 4 ft. high and 8 ft. long, with an average piece length of 16 in. Divide this length (16 in.) into the full cord length of 48 in. and multiply by the price.

48 ÷ 16 = 3 x $55 = $165.
Therefore, dealer A sells firewood for $165 per cord.

Dealer B sells what he calls a "stove cord" for $45. It is a pile measuring 4 ft. by 8 ft. with an average length of 12 in. The calculation is:
48 ÷ 12 = 4 x $45 = $180.
Therefore, dealer B sells firewood for $180 per cord.

Dealer C sells a 4 ft. x 8 ft. x 18 in "face cord" for $60. The result is:
48 ÷ 18 = 2.66 x $60 = $159.60
Therefore, dealer C sells firewood for $159.60 per cord.

Tips on Buying Firewood

If possible, avoid buying firewood in units that cannot be related to the standard full cord. Pickup truck loads and station wagon loads are impossible to measure and can be more expensive than cord measures of wood.

You can usually find firewood dealers in the yellow pages of the telephone directory or by referral from neighbours who purchase firewood. If possible, go to the supplier's yard and see the wood before you buy. Measure the average piece length to be sure it will fit in your appliance and check that all pieces are close to the same length. Look for a range of piece sizes, with no pieces larger than 150 mm (6 in.) in diameter.

If you want to process the firewood yourself, you could consider buying the wood in log lengths or getting a fuel wood permit from the local office of your provincial natural resources ministry. Sawmills may also have cut-offs, slabs and cull logs that they will sell for firewood.

You can save money by processing the firewood yourself. Get together with neighbours, buy a large truckload, rent a splitter and process the wood cooperatively.

Firewood is measured in cords. A cord measures 1.2 m x 1.2 m x 2.4 m (4 x 4 x 8 ft.). Many firewood dealers sell part-cords called face cords or stove cords. Pictured below are three "face" cords with pieces measuring an average of 16 in. Together, these three face cords make up one full cord.

How Much is Enough?

Only experience will tell you how much wood you will need for a winter's supply. A medium-sized modern home, if heated exclusively with wood, would need between two and four full cords. In the same house, a space heater used for part of the heating load may use only one or two full cords, while reducing conventional fuel use by more than 50 per cent. Considerably more wood will be needed in very cold areas, in large, leaky houses, or where softwoods are used. Properly-stored firewood will not rot in a year, so buying a little extra is a good idea.

Buying and Storing Pellet Fuel

Pellet fuel is normally purchased in 18 kg (40 lb.) plastic bags. Householders who heat full time in winter with pellet stoves or furnaces usually buy their pellets by the tonne and have it delivered in the fall.

Wood pellets should be stored indoors and be kept off concrete floors on skids. If pellet fuel is exposed to moisture the pellets swell up and become unusable. Before accepting a shipment of pellets, check the contents of a sample bag to see that the pellets retain their shiny outer surface, indicating that they have not been exposed to moisture.

*THE FIREWOOD CORD – Firewood is measured in cords. A **full** cord measures 1.2 m x 2.4 m x 1.2 m (4 ft. x 8 ft. x 4 ft.). Many firewood dealers sell partial cords called face or stove cords. Pictured are three face cords with pieces measuring an average of 40 cm (16 in.). Together, these three face cords make up one full cord and should equal 3.6 m³ (128 cubic feet).*

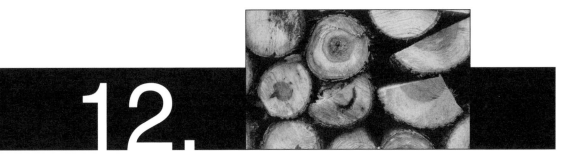

12.

MAINTAINING YOUR WOOD-HEATING SYSTEM

Wood-heat system maintenance includes simple tasks such as ash removal and glass cleaning, as well as bigger jobs such as chimney cleaning, gasket replacement, repainting and major repairs.

Wood-heat system maintenance includes simple tasks such as ash removal and glass cleaning, as well as bigger jobs such as chimney cleaning, gasket replacement, repainting and major repairs.

Wood-burning systems operate under a variety of conditions during each heating season, and these different conditions create the need for various maintenance tasks. For example, the slower burning needed in fall and spring when heat demand is low, tends to result in more rapid creosote build-up in the flue pipe and chimney. Chimney cleaning is usually needed more often in spring and fall, especially for older appliances that do not burn the wood completely. On the other hand, wood-burning appliances operate closer to their maximum heat output during the coldest winter months which causes stress to parts that are exposed to high heat. Advanced-technology wood heaters have internal parts that wear out because of their exposure to high temperatures. In good quality appliances, any part that can wear due to normal use is replaceable.

One of the best ways to be sure that your wood heating system gets the maintenance it needs is to hire a professional chimney sweep who is trained and certified under the WETT program. A professional sweep will clean the system from top to bottom and report any problems to you. The sweep might suggest that it is time to replace the flue pipes, catalytic combustor, or door gaskets, and will probably be able to do the work for you when the time comes. Your WETT-certified wood heating retailer may also offer sweeping and maintenance services.

Here are the most important maintenance tasks to consider as you look over the condition of your wood heating system:

Clean and inspect the chimney and flue pipes

The chimney and flue pipes must be checked regularly until the rate of creosote build-up is determined. Chimney fires usually happen because the user was surprised at how fast the deposits developed. Check the pipes often and clean when the deposits have built up to more than 4 mm (1/8 in.). Older systems that smoulder can need cleaning as often as every few weeks. Advanced-technology appliances can operate so efficiently that cleaning is only needed once a year. However, even if you have an advanced stove, never assume the chimney is clean. Check it often to be sure.

As maintenance is done, it is a good idea to check the condition of the chimney and flue pipes to see if there is any deterioration. Check the flue pipes for rust that can weaken the joints. Look for corrosion or rust stains on the outer shell of a metal chimney, and check for bulges or corrosion in its liner. When inspecting a masonry chimney, look for black or white stains on the outer bricks, and cracks or missing

pieces in the chimney liner. Always check the condition of the chimney in hidden spaces including the attic, wall and chimney chase areas where corrosion and other deterioration can occur.

The most thorough cleaning and inspection of the appliance and venting system should be done in the late spring just after the heating season is over. Deposits left in the appliance can combine with the warm humid summer air to cause corrosion of steel parts. Cleaning and inspection in spring will also give you plenty of time to order replacement parts and do any needed repairs before the fall heating season begins. If you see any problems during your cleaning and inspection, have the system thoroughly inspected by a qualified chimney sweep and repaired before continuing to use it.

Check firebricks, baffle plates and catalytic combustors

Cracked firebricks don't necessarily need immediate replacement, but if bricks start to break up, they should be replaced right away because they protect the steel parts from being damaged by heat.

Baffles are steel, ceramic or firebrick plates within the stove that divert the exhaust to take a longer path before exiting at the flue collar. Because of their location and function, baffles can deteriorate with use. Any warping or breakage of a baffle is a sign that it needs replacement. Some appliances have air tubes at the top of their fireboxes that may also deteriorate. It is important to immediately repair any damage to baffles or air tubes because continued use could do permanent damage to parts that cannot be replaced.

Catalytic combustors deteriorate slowly over their expected life span of two to six years. Follow the manufacturer's instructions for the annual maintenance of the combustor. Visible smoke from the chimney may be the first indication that the combustor has stopped working. To check its function, start a fire and warm the stove normally. Engage the combustor by closing the bypass damper and set the air control for an extended burn cycle. Wait 15 minutes then go outside to see if there is visible smoke coming from the chimney. If you see smoke, check with your wood heat dealer or chimney sweep on further advice on when to replace the combustor.

Replace door gaskets and other seals

Gaskets and seals are important because they control the location and flow rates of air into the appliance. Leaky seals will reduce the efficiency of the unit. Some gaskets may need replacement as often as once each year, and others may be fine for several years of use. The glass panels in stove and fireplace doors also have gaskets that should be replaced when the door gasket is replaced. All gaskets and seals should be checked at least once a year during a thorough maintenance inspection and perhaps once again during the heating season. You can do a quick check of door gasket seals when the appliance is not operating by closing the door on a thin piece of paper. When the door is latched closed, the paper should be gripped firmly by the door seal. Do this test all the way around the door. If the paper pulls out easily, either the door latch needs adjustment or the gasket needs replacement.

To get a good seal with gaskets, the correct size and type must be used. Follow the manufacturer's instructions for gasket selection and, if possible, go back to the retailer that sold the unit to buy gasket material and glue. Some retailers offer a gasket replacement service in which you bring in your appliance door and the staff installs the correct door and glass gaskets for you.

Maintaining door glass

The door glass in modern wood burners is actually a transparent ceramic material that can withstand very high temperatures. It is unlikely that the glass will break because of heat, but if it is struck with a hard object, it can break. Always go back to the store where you bought the appliance or to its manufacturer for replacement glass so you are sure to get the right size, shape and material.

Most new appliances have an air-wash system to keep the glass clear, but these systems vary in effectiveness. Some door glass panels stay clear for weeks, while others get hazy within a few days. Wait until the appliance has cooled before cleaning the glass. Usually, a damp cloth or paper towel will remove the ash dust or light stains. To remove darker more stubborn stains, see your stove retailer for the special stove glass cleaner that removes the stains and does not scratch the surface. Apply the cleaner to the cloth, rather than spraying it on the glass to avoid having it drip onto the gasket where it may cause deterioration. Dark streaks forming from the edge of the glass panel are a sign that the door glass gasket needs replacing.

Service fans and other components

Stove, fireplace and furnace fans can pick up dust and hair which can cause wear and reduce their efficiency. Any fan that is used regularly should be cleaned at least once each year. The fan motor may need lubricating and the fan enclosure should be vacuumed.

Maintenance tasks for pellet stoves

Pellet stoves are more complex than wood stoves, with motors, fans, electronic controls and heat exchangers. Most pellet stoves need cleaning every four to six weeks or after having burned about one tonne of pellets. This servicing includes cleaning of the firebox walls, heat exchanger, ash pan and burn pot of ash deposits. Clean the hopper of pellet dust, and, in the case of a stove with a gasket on the fuel hopper lid, clear this area of pellet chips and dust. The venting system may need cleaning each month if a high-ash grade of wood pellets is being burned. Hearth shops offer vacuum cleaners that are specifically designed for pellet stove maintenance.

At the end of each heating season a more thorough servicing is needed. The pellet stove installation manual outlines the steps to be followed for this annual service. The venting system is usually cleaned thoroughly and re-sealed at the end of the heating season. Fan and auger motors may need oiling, and deposits should be removed from fan blades. The component compartment of the stove should be vacuumed and the stove re-assembled. Glass and door gaskets should be checked and replaced when required.

Many people choose to do the periodic cleanings on their own, while having a qualified technician complete the more complex annual cleaning. The efficient operation and durability of pellet appliances depends on proper servicing periodically during use as well as the major servicing at the end of the heating season.

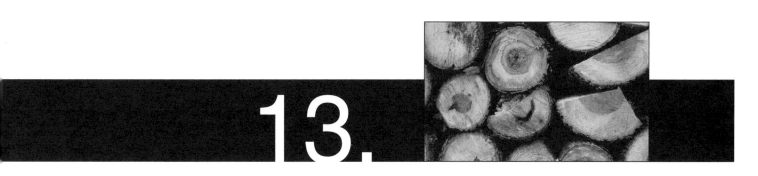

13.

HEARTH ACCESSORIES

There are some accessories that are necessary for successful and convenient wood heating. There are other accessories that may seem like a good idea, but can create problems.

There are some accessories that are necessary for successful and convenient wood heating. There are other accessories that may seem like a good idea, but can create problems. Here is a review of some of the options.

Fire Tool Set

You will need a tool set to manage the fire and keep the hearth neat. In general, tool sets for wood heating are simpler and shorter in length than sets for fireplaces. The set should have three tools: a rake for moving charcoal and logs around, a brush and a shovel. A rake is more useful for managing a heating fire than a poker. Pokers and tongs are better for conventional fireplaces.

Ash Container

Ashes should be taken outside as soon as they are removed from the appliance because they may release toxic carbon monoxide into the indoor air. The outside ash storage container should be metal, have a tight-fitting lid, and it should be placed on concrete away from combustible materials. If your appliance doesn't have an ash pan, you will also need a small ash bucket for transferring ash from the appliance to the outside ash storage can.

Removing ash can result in a lot of dust being released into the house. There are a couple of ways to reduce the amount of ash dust released. If you must shovel ash into a bucket, use a small bucket that you can hold in the door opening so that most of the ash dust is drawn back into the stove. This only works if there is still an active bed of charcoal at the back of the firebox to provide enough heat to produce draft. In other words, the hardest time to control ash dust is when the appliance is cold because there is no chimney draft to draw dust back through the opening. Another option is a ash device that can scoop out ash through the door opening. Ask your wood heat retailer about an ash scoop with a sliding lid.

Hearth Gloves

A pair of heat-resistant gloves is handy to have near the hearth. Gloves can be worn when you need to rake a large coal bed, or in an emergency such as picking up a log that has rolled out of the firebox. Hearth gloves are lined, thick leather gloves with long cuffs. Wood heat dealers usually carry hearth gloves, and welding supply stores have gloves that work well for use around stoves and fireplaces.

Fire Screen

Heating stoves and fireplaces should be operated with their doors closed and latched to produce high efficiency and low smoke emissions. However, some manufacturers offer accessory screens that can be put in place when the door is fully opened. The use of fire screens in modern stoves and fireplaces should be minimized for three reasons. First, having the door open disables the combustion system, meaning that smoke emissions are much higher than with the door closed. Second, the open door makes the appliance much more likely to spill smoke into the room, causing indoor air pollution. Third, the efficiency of the stove or fireplace falls to very low levels when the door is open, meaning that much of the energy in the firewood is wasted.

Domestic Hot Water Coil or Collector

Many people who heat with wood like the idea of heating their domestic hot water (DHW) with their wood-heating appliance. This is done with a water coil or collector in the firebox or attached to the hot outside surface of the appliance. However there are a few reasons why the heating of domestic hot water is rare. First, no advanced, low-emission stoves, fireplaces or furnaces are certified to use a DHW collector because the heat drawn away from the combustion zone would make it impossible to meet EPA's emission limits. Second, DHW systems linked to wood-heating appliances can be very complex and expensive. Third, because of the risks of steam explosions and water damage, home insurance companies are sometimes reluctant to provide insurance coverage to homes containing such systems. Some cook stove manufacturers offer DHW collector accessories and wood-fired boilers can usually be adapted easily to heat DHW. Be sure that the DHW collector you are considering is certified for use with your appliance.

Humidifier

Many people who heat with wood use a kettle of water on their stoves to add moisture to the often dry winter air. Suitable kettles or humidifiers can be found in most wood-heating retail stores. The kettle should be placed on a grille or trivet rather than directly on the stove surface. The trivet will prevent moisture condensation during cooling cycles and rust from forming on the stove top.

Not all houses need extra moisture in winter. New, tightly constructed houses with low air leakage rates don't need extra moisture because normal household activities such as washing and cooking add enough moisture. The best way to check if your house needs extra humidity is to buy an inexpensive hygrometer, sometimes called a relative humidity indicator. Once you know how your house functions in winter you can decide if more humidity is needed.

14.

COMPARING ANNUAL HEATING COSTS

You may be interested in calculating the cost of using wood fuel compared to the conventional fuels such as oil, natural gas, propane or electricity. The procedure outlined here can provide comparative figures.

You may be interested in calculating the cost of using wood fuel compared to the conventional fuels such as oil, natural gas, propane or electricity. The procedure outlined here can provide comparative figures. However, no calculation can account for all the variables involved when a wood heating system is installed. For example, this procedure is based on the fuel consumption of central heating systems that heat all areas of the house to the same temperature, whereas most people who heat with wood keep their main living areas much warmer than bedrooms and utility areas. As a result, the savings that could result from the installation of a wood stove to supplement the heat provided by another fuel cannot be estimated accurately using this procedure.

If you are unsure if you can save money by burning wood, your own community can help to provide the answer. Piles of firewood standing in yards in your neighbourhood are an indication that some households heat with wood. You might ask neighbours who have wood heating systems whether they actually save money by heating with wood. Direct advice from people who live near you may be more accurate than a calculated number.

Here is a tip on how to make the calculation more accurate for your situation. If you know how much money you spent on another energy source last year, you could test the accuracy of the heat load and house type figures for your area. If the resulting cost is more than you spent, lower the house heat load figure until the calculation matches the amount you spent. Then you can calculate your wood heating costs more accurately.

Step 1: The Price of Fuels in Your Area

Call your local fuel suppliers to find out the average cost of fuels. The cost should be the total cost as delivered to your home. Be sure to get the prices in the same units for the fuel as shown in Table 1. Write the costs in the spaces provided.

Note that the figures for natural firewood fuel are for full 4 x 4 x 8 ft. cords. The energy content figures are in metric units called megajoules (MJ).

Step 2: Typical Seasonal Efficiency of Appliance Types

Choose the types of equipment you want to compare from the list of systems in Table 2. Note the efficiency figures for the equipment in the right-hand column. Using these efficiency figures, you can calculate the savings you can achieve by upgrading an older system to a newer, more efficient appliance.

Table 1

ENERGY SOURCE	ENERGY CONTENT	YOUR LOCAL PRICE
Oil	38.2 MJ/Litre	/litre
Electricity	3.6 MJ/kWh	/kWh
Natural Gas	37.5 MJ/m³	/m³
Propane	25.3/MJ/litre	/litre
Hardwood (air dried)	30 600 MJ/cord	/cord
Softwood (air dried)	18 700 MJ/cord	/cord
Mixed Fuelwood (air dried)	25 000 MJ/cord	/cord
Wood Pellets	19 800 MJ/tonne	/tonne

Energy Content and Local Price of Various Fuels

Table 2

FUEL	TYPE OF SYSTEM	EFFICIENCY%
Oil (furnace or boiler)	Cast Iron Head Burner (pre 1970)	60
	Retention Head Burner	70 - 78
	Mid-efficiency Furnace or boiler	83 - 89
Electricity	Furnace/Boiler or Baseboard	100
	Geothermal (ground source heat pump)	260
Natural Gas	Furnace/Boiler - conventional	55 - 65
	- mid-efficiency	78 - 84
	- condensing	90 - 97
Propane	Furnace/boiler - conventional	55 - 65
	- mid-efficiency	79 - 85
	- condensing	88 - 95
Wood Conventional	Furnace/Boiler	45 - 55
	Advanced* Furnace/Boiler	55 - 65
	Conventional Stove (properly located)	50 - 65
	Advanced* Stove (properly located)	65 - 80
	Advanced* Fireplace	50 - 70
Wood	Pellet Stove	55 - 80

Typical Seasonal Heating System Efficiencies

* Advanced refers to appliances certified as low-emissions by the EPA or according to the CSA B415.1 standard.

	Table 3			
CITY	TOWN HOUSE	NEW SEMI-DETACHED	NEW DETACHED	OLD DETACHED
Victoria/Vancouver	30	45	60	85
Prince George	60	80	110	150
Calgary	50	65	90	120
Edmonton	55	70	95	130
Grand Prairie/Pr. Albert	60	80	105	140
Regina/Saskatoon	50	70	90	130
Winnipeg	50	70	90	130
Whitehorse	60	85	115	155
Yellowknife	80	110	145	195
Thunder Bay	55	70	95	130
Sudbury	50	65	90	120
Ottawa	40	55	75	110
Toronto	35	45	65	95
Windsor	30	40	55	80
Montréal	45	60	80	110
Québec City	50	65	85	115
Chicoutimi	55	70	90	125
Saint John	45	60	75	105
Edmundston	50	65	90	120
Charlottetown	45	60	80	110
Halifax	40	55	75	100
St. John's	45	60	85	120

Typical Heating Loads in gigajoules (GJ) for Various Housing Types in Canadian Cities

Step 3: Housing Type and Heating Loads

From the list of cities and housing types in Table 3, select the combination that is the closest to your area and house type. The heating load figures are in metric units called gigajoules. One gigajoule equals 1000 megajoules.

Notes:
1. Town House - inside unit, approximately 1000 square feet
2. New Semi-Detached - approximately 1500 square feet
3. New Detached House - approximately 2000 square feet
4. Old Detached House - approximately 2000 square feet

Step 4: Calculation Using the Formula

The annual heating cost is calculated as follows:

$$\frac{\text{Energy Cost/Unit}}{\text{Energy Content}} \times \frac{\text{Heating Load}}{\text{System Efficiency}} \times 100\,000 = \text{Approximate Annual Heating Cost}$$

Enter the cost per unit of energy and divide it by the energy content of the fuel (both figures come from Table 1). Select the heating load for your location and housing type from Table 3 and divide it by the efficiency of the proposed heating system from Table 2. Multiply the results of these two calculations, then multiply that result by 100,000.

Sample Calculation

Here are the details of the sample calculation:
Location: near Halifax, N.S.
House type: new detached, heating load 75
Type and cost of existing fuel: oil at $1.12/L
Type and cost of proposed fuel: mixed hardwood at $250/cord
Type and efficiency of existing heating system: oil furnace 80%
Type and efficiency of proposed heating system: advanced wood stove 70%

The calculation of the cost of oil heating would be:
(1.12 ÷ 38.23) x (75 ÷ 80) x 100,000 = $2,747.
The calculation of the cost of wood heating using mixed firewood would be:
(300 ÷ 25,000) x (75 ÷ 70) x 100,000 = $1286.

In this example, if the wood stove displaced all of the oil previously used for heating, the annual savings would be $1,461.

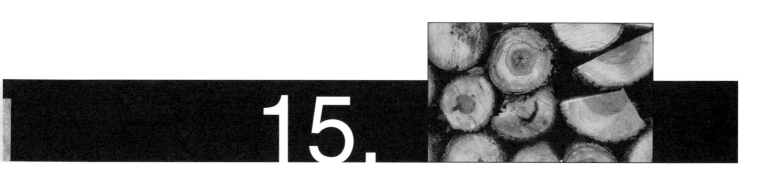

15.

FOR MORE INFORMATION

Fuel wood

Products, Services and Safety Information

Safety Information

Publications

Fuel wood

- Provincial ministries of natural resources
- In your local telephone directory, under "Firewood"

Products, Services and Safety Information

- Seek out people who are WETT-certified for information and services.
  On the Web: www.wettinc.ca

   In your local telephone directory, look for this logo under "Chimneys," "Chimney Cleaning," "Heating Contractors," "Fireplaces" and "Wood Stoves – Retail"

- In Quebec seek out people who are trained and certified by L'Association des professionnels du chauffage (APC)

  On the Web: www.poelesfoyers.ca

   Look for this logo in your local telephone directory under "Chimneys," "Chimney Cleaning," "Heating Contractors," "Fireplaces" and "Wood Stoves - Retail" ("Cheminées", "Cheminées - Ramonage", "Chauffage - Entrepreneurs", "Foyers" et "Poêles à Bois - Détaillants")

Safety Information

- Your local municipal office for building inspection and fire inspection
- Provincial Fire Marshal's Office

Publications

- For additional copies of this publication or other publications on housing, write to:
  Canada Mortgage and Housing Corporation
  Canadian Housing Information Centre
  700 Montreal Road
  Ottawa, Ontario
  K1A 0P7
  Tel: (613) 748-2367
  Fax: (613) 748-4069

Notes

Notes